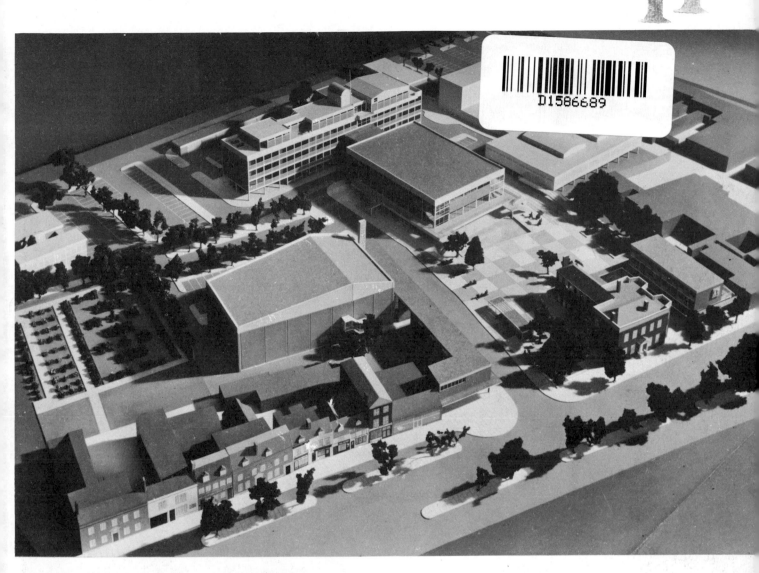

The film set of about 1920 (opposite) must have seemed a fantastic and frightening prospect at the time, but we have now come to understand that human environment may indeed assume this appearance if we are too much preoccupied with mechanical and commercial efficiency at the expense of human efficiency. Whether they are designing towns (above) or machines (left), the best designers seek to create a truly human environment through a sensitive use of modern technology.

BAKER.

THE SHAPES WE NEED

by Kurt Rowland MSIA

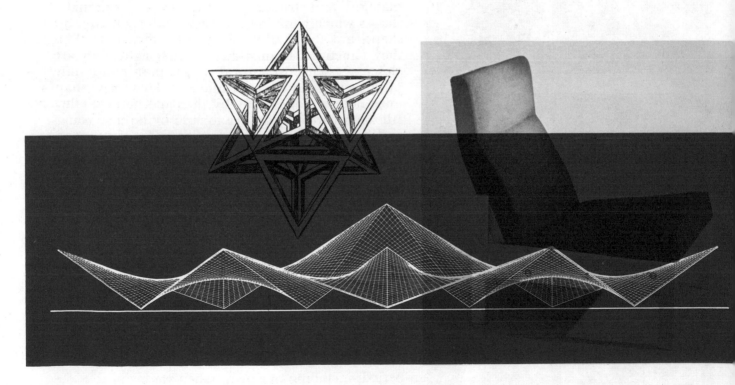

Ginn and Company Ltd.

18 Bedford Row

London WC1

About this book

Part One of *Looking and Seeing* established certain basic principles which are essential to any visual understanding of the world around us. It showed that no single element in our surroundings can be considered in isolation, and that such related subjects as materials, production methods, function, environment, and social conditions have a far-reaching influence on our ability to make visual assessments. Part Two examined these ideas a little more closely. Together Parts One and Two provide a kind of visual grammar which serves as a basis for the more complicated ideas discussed in this book and in Part Four.

During the twentieth century our man-made environment has undergone a profound change. Whereas in the past the process of trial and error played an important part in the development of each object, today our scientific and mathematical knowledge enables us to foretell the behaviour of materials and structures and to arrive at original shapes which combine precision with economy. Such shapes are above all mechanically efficient. Although they sometimes seem strange at first sight, they are closer in essence to natural shapes than many things produced before the scientific era. These new shapes must not be judged only by their mechanical efficiency. All man-made objects are for use by human beings, and because they form part of man's environment have a deep effect on him. The best of them therefore need to combine mechanical efficiency with human efficiency. This, broadly speaking, is the purpose of design.

There is a third element in the creation of the human environment. The collective outlook on life of the people of every age, their opinions, beliefs and attitudes, produce the atmosphere in which their environment is created. This collective outlook influences the production of each man-made object, and gives the many different objects made in any one age an underlying unity. Every age has its own character, expressed through its own visual language. We can find new meaning in the productions of any period, including our own, when we begin to understand its visual language. The modern world will not become a coherent whole until all of us— users as well as designers—master the visual language of our own times.

Contents

© K. F. Rowland 1965
156501
Printed in Great Britain
by W. S. Cowell Ltd,
at the Butter Market, Ipswich

Mathematics in our surroundings

Picture 1 shows a famous building in Rome: the Tempietto, built by the architect Bramante in 1502. Its fame rests above all on the harmonious relationship between height and width, not only in the building as a whole, but in its individual parts. If any one of these relationships were disturbed, the harmonious appearance of the whole building would suffer. In 2, one of these relationships, that between the height and the width of the columns, has been changed, and as a result the building has lost its harmony and perfection. If you changed any other ratio the result would be similar. The harmonious relationship between the ratios of a building can be referred to as its proportions. We all have a natural feeling for ratios and proportions. As we shall see, there is a mathematical explanation of this feeling.

Imagine you are walking over a large field which stretches as far as you can see. In the distance an object looms above the horizon. As the light is failing you cannot recognise what it is, nor observe its colour or the texture of its surface. You do not know what material it is made of. Since there are no other objects about, such as trees or people, and you do not know how far away it is, you cannot judge its size. But in spite of this a part of the object's character will have impressed itself on you; you will have compared its height with its width. As you approach the object and recognise all the qualities of the object you will add further impressions until your idea of the object's character is fairly complete. But your first impression – comparison of height with width – will have conveyed to you an important part of the object's character.

We observe and experience all the shapes of our surroundings in this way. Whether we are looking at motor cars or animals, a comparison of height with width gives us a part of the object's character. It can be expressed in terms of mathematics and is called a ratio. As we look at the world about us we often compare the ratio of one shape with the ratio of another. This is a more complicated but quite common experience which occurs to all of us much more often than we realise.

1

2

For an experiment a number of people were asked to draw a jug on a piece of paper. All the pieces of paper were of the same size and shape. After the drawings had been collected the same people were asked to draw the same jug again, with the sheet of paper turned by 90 degrees. None of these people were professional artists or draughtsmen. When the two sets of drawings were compared it was found that the average drawing of the jug tended to follow the shape of the paper, **3**, **4**, that is to say it was taller when the paper was used upright and squatter when the paper was used horizontally. Each draughtsman unconsciously tried to bring about a harmonious relationship between the ratio of the paper and that of the jug. It is natural for human beings to try and find harmonious relationships between ratios in this way.

To test people's feeling for ratio, let us ask a number of people to divide a line so that a pleasing relationship exists between the two parts. Here you can see how some of them will do it. To halve anything exactly is not very interesting; to have one very large and one very small piece is too unbalanced and therefore also unsatisfactory; most people will compromise between these two extremes and divide the line as shown in **5**. If you took a very large number of samples and averaged them out you would get the result shown in **6**. Most people find this a particularly happy division, in which neither part is too small or too large. We can say that the two parts of the line harmonise; that their relationship is satisfactory.

A similar test can be applied to rectangular shapes. A great number of people were shown a range of rectangles and asked to choose the one which they thought was the most perfect shape, that is to say in which the greatest harmony existed between the long and the short sides. This diagram, **7**, shows what their answers were. An overwhelming majority preferred one rectangle, or its immediate, very similar neighbours, to all the others, which makes one wonder what special qualities this favourite rectangle has. If you compare the ratio of the long to the short sides you will find it is the ratio of our divided line, **6**. It appears that this ratio is preferred by most people.

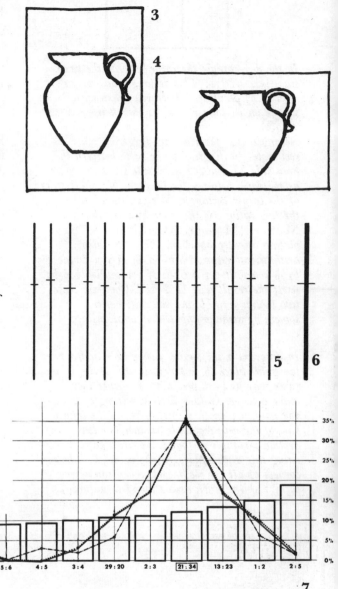

*Diagram **7** shows the result of the test to find the favourite rectangle. Men's preferences (black line) vary from women's (red line). You can see the vast majority of both men and women preferred this rectangle or its immediate neighbours.*

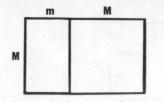

In the φ rectangle the ratio between the two sides is 1·618:1. This rectangle has a number of peculiarities. If you construct a square on its longer side, as shown in diagram **1**, the square taken together with the rectangle will form a new, larger φ rectangle. In diagram **1** the ratio between the long side M and the short side m is the same as the ratio between the long and the short sides of the larger rectangle. We can show that the two ratios are the same by writing M:m = (M + m):M. *This is a mathematical proportion. There are also arithmetical relationships in φ. If you divide 1 by φ you will get 0·618. If you multiply φ by itself the result will be 2·618. Compare these two figures with φ and you will notice something strange about their relationship.*

In diagram **2** the square **a** has been added to the small black φ rectangle in the centre, in the same way as in diagram **1**. Together they make a larger Golden Section rectangle. If you now add another square, **b**, on the longer side of the new rectangle another Golden Section rectangle is found. You can go on doing this with squares **c**, **d**, **e** and **f**. The corners of all the rectangles, when connected, form a spiral, such as we found in natural shapes.

If you compared the two parts of the divided line or two sides of the favourite rectangle you would find that the longer is approximately 1·618 times as long as the shorter. In other words the ratio between them is 1·618:1. This ratio may be written as 1·618, a number which has many fascinating qualities first noticed by Euclid, the father of modern geometry, about the year 300 B.C. It has always been considered an important number: mathematicians have given it the name φ (pronounced fie); the artists of the Renaissance called it the Divine Proportion; the Greeks used the pentagon, which includes a number of φ relationships, as a holy symbol.

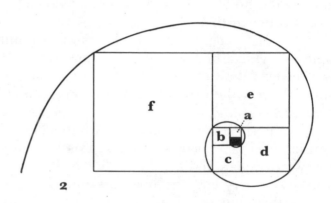

2

3

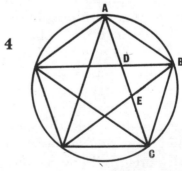

4

In the pentagon, **4**, there is a Golden Section relationship between any diagonal and any side of the pentagon. AC:AB = φ. All the diagonals intersect each other according to the Golden Section, so that AD:DE = φ and CE:ED = φ. The smaller, inner pentagon formed by the diagonals contains similar relationships which can be expressed by φ. It is easy to understand why the Greeks thought the pentagon such a perfect shape and used it as a sacred symbol.

This wonderful number, which is also known as the Golden Section, the Golden Ratio, or the Golden Number, has more than mathematical applications; it is also significant in the living world. We can see that natural organisms, including the human body, are really based on the φ relationship. In preferring proportions based on φ we are therefore following natural laws.

We have seen how artists have always sought to establish relationships in their works, and some of these relationships can be expressed by ratios. The plans and drawings of the architecture of past ages show how preoccupied architects have always been with the problem of ratio, not only of the overall shape of a building but also of the smaller shapes. They considered the ratios of windows and doors and related them to the ratios of the outside walls. They also calculated the height, length and width of each room in relation to each other. A building then was a most complicated system of ratios. In order to make it possible to arrive at a set of perfect proportions, they often related their measurements to φ. In some cases they found φ just as easily, by instinct, as the people in the experiment described on page 5, in other cases all the relationships were worked out by mathematics. In this way they created buildings and other works whose ratios were related to each other and through φ to the living world.

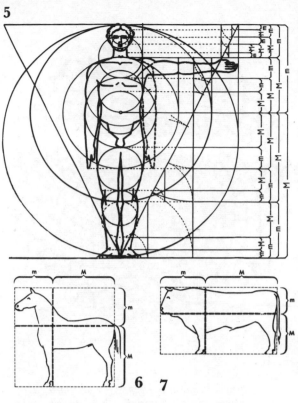

5

6 7

The φ proportion also appears in the human body and many living things. In diagrams 5, 6, and 7, each pair of dimensions marked M m forms a Golden Proportion. Diagram 9 is the same as the grid in picture 10. The following are some of the Golden Proportions which can be recognised: AB:BC, BD:ED, DC:FC, ED:DF, DG:DF, FC:GC, HC:JK, JK:LM, LM:NO.

8

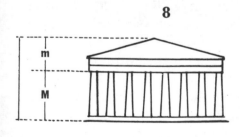

9

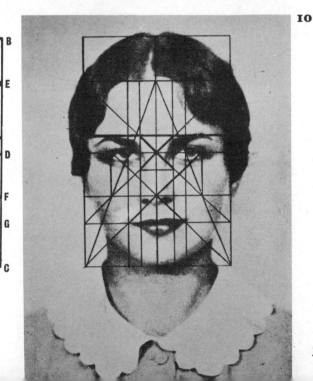

10

The Golden Section was also much in evidence in Greek architecture, 8. But artists of all ages have used the Golden Section quite instinctively, as did the people in the experiment on page 5. In the painting by Seurat, 3, the most pronounced horizontal divides the upright edge of the picture according to the Golden Section.

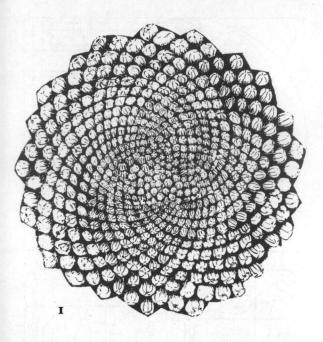

1

Can you find an interesting relationship in this series of numbers?

1 1 2 3 5 8 13 21 34 55 89 144

Each number is the sum of the two which precede it. This is a Fibonacci series, called after Fibonacci (1170-1250), the mathematician who first used it. But there is something even more important contained in the Fibonacci series. Examine the ratios between any number of the series and the preceding one: for instance 34 and 21, and work out their ratio by dividing the higher number by the lower.

$$\begin{array}{r} 1.6190 \\ 21 \overline{)\ 34} \end{array}$$

Repeat this with higher numbers in the series, say 144 and 89.

$$\begin{array}{r} 1.6179 \\ 89 \overline{)\ 144} \end{array}$$

You will notice that the higher you go the closer the ratio will be to the Golden Ratio of ϕ. Mathematicians know that however high you go in the series, ϕ is never reached exactly, any more than the people on page 5 attempting to divide a line in this ratio found the exact point, although they were always very near it. But the Fibonacci series is not merely an interesting series of figures; it can be found in many aspects of the living world.

Let us look once more at the pyrethrum which you have already seen in Part One (page 84). This diagram, **1**, shows clearly how two sets of spirals intersect to form the pattern. You will see that the number of spirals is not the same in the two sets; there are in fact 21 right-hand spirals and 34 left-hand ones. Can you find these two numbers in the Fibonacci series?

This is not the only arrangement of spirals in this variety of pyrethrum and you may find an occasional flower with a spiral more or less in one direction or the other, but well over 90 per cent of all the variety will conform to this pattern, so that we may regard it as normal, and the others as exceptions. In certain varieties of sunflower you will find combinations of 34 and 55 spirals, or 55 and 89, or even 89 and 144. These, too, you will notice are Fibonacci numbers.

*Spirals in natural shapes, **1**, are normally arranged in Fibonacci numbers, which are also important to the proportions of the human body, **2**. Nature is full of such relationships. In most cases they can only be sensed, but here we see some of them expressed in numbers and mathematical terms.*

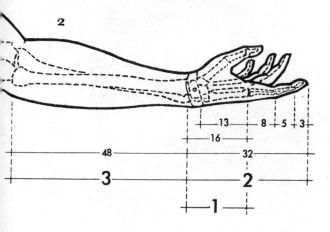

2

The Norway spruce cone has its spirals arranged in sets of 5 and 8. A daisy has sets of 13 and 21. A small flower like the ranunculus has 2 spirals going in one direction and 3 in the other.

All these numbers are part of the Fibonacci series, which, as you read opposite, is linked to the Golden Number ϕ. We can see now that many of the relationships in nature which without mathematics we could do no more than sense, can in fact be expressed in mathematical terms. Le Corbusier, the architect whose Ronchamp chapel you read about in Part Two, has said: 'Mathematics is the majestic structure conceived by man to grant him comprehension of the universe.' Nature is a logical system and only a study of mathematics will reveal certain of its secrets.

*Both the pine cone, **3**, and the dahlia, **4**, have two sets of spirals. Count them and see if they are part of the Fibonacci series.*

4

3

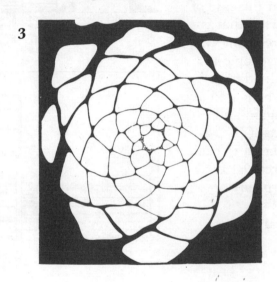

*Nobody would suspect a plant like **5** to have anything to do with mathematics; it seems to be too unorganised and irregular. But a simple investigation of its structure and manner of growing, **6**, reveals the Fibonacci series.*

5

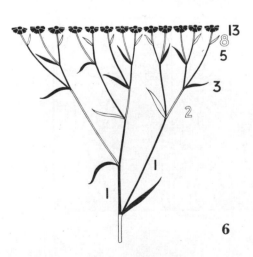

6

Le Corbusier devised a system of proportions and measurements which he called the Modulor. This consists of two sets of figures. The first is based on the height of the average man (1·829 metres, or 1829 millimetres). If this height is divided according to the Golden Section (see page 6), the longer of the two parts will be 1130 millimetres. This also corresponds to the navel height, as we have already seen in diagram **6** on page 7. This height can again be divided according to the Golden Section, when the figure 698 millimetres will be obtained for the longer part. We can go on dividing and subdividing according to φ until a whole range of figures is found. This is column A in diagram **1**. Column B is obtained in the same way, but in this case the starting point is the height of the average man with his arm stretched up. This dimension is divided again and again as in the case of column A. Each column is a Fibonacci series, that is to say each figure is the sum of the two preceding it. The Golden Section, which is felt by most people to be the most natural and pleasant way of dividing a line or constructing a rectangle, and for which we have also found a mathematical basis, is used again and again in the Modulor to provide two series of measurements which are harmoniously related to each other. As diagram **3** shows, they are also related to important points of the human frame. Furniture designed to these measurements, **2**, can therefore be both harmonious and practical at the same time.

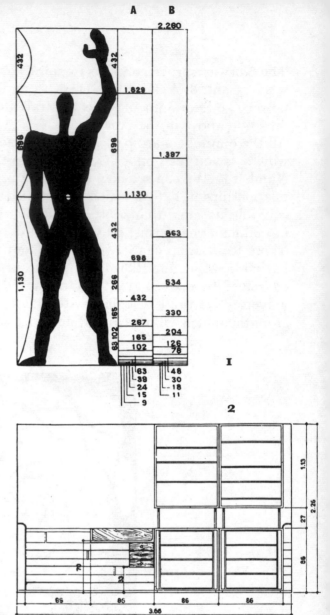

1

2

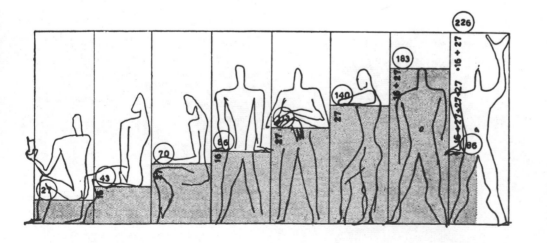

3

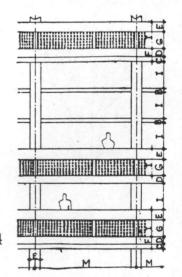

4

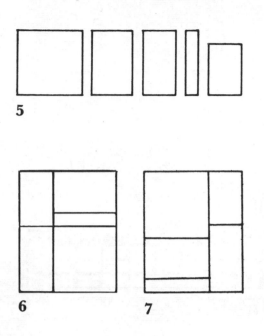

5

6   **7**

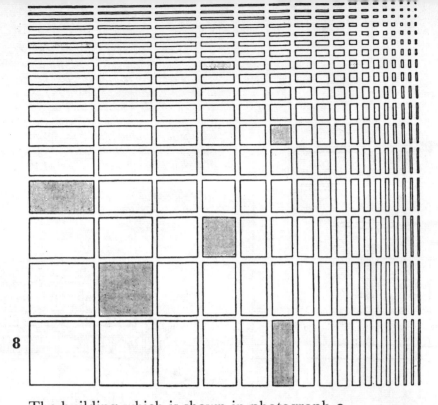

8

The grid, 8, is based on a set of measurements from the Modulor. Different panels taken from it, 5, are easily fitted together, 6, 7. Also, any large panel can easily be divided into a number of smaller ones. This is due to the fact that in a Fibonacci series each number is the sum of preceding numbers. Can you think where this might be particularly useful?

The building which is shown in photograph **9** was designed by Le Corbusier with the help of the Modulor. In the drawing of a detail of the building, **4**, the architect has taken all the dimensions from either series A or B of the Modulor.

In our age of technology, when many parts of a building are mass-produced, often in different factories, such a system of measuring is especially important, as the different parts can be made to fit quite easily. But as well as enabling us to reap the full benefit of mass-production it will also help us to produce things which satisfy the requirements of our bodies and minds. The great quality of the Modulor is that it grapples with the special problems of our age.

9

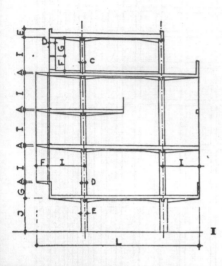

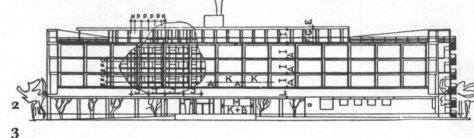

*The factory, **1, 2, 3**, by Le Corbusier, shows many applications of his Modulor. The letters in the drawing can be referred to the two columns of figures. If you look at them closely you will find that these figures come from the Modulor (**1**, page 10) but the last decimal has been ignored in each case. The sectional drawing, **1**, shows also that throughout the depth of the building dimensions are derived from the Modulor. The measurements of all three dimensions are therefore related.*

A		78
B		33
C	43	
D		53
E	70	
F	113	
G	183	
H		226
I	296	
J		366
K		592
L	1254	
M	625 =	K + B
N		86
P		140

There are many more relationships in nature which can be seen to have a mathematical link. If we draw a grid of lines as shown in **4**, and then draw a similar grid but with smaller distances between the vertical lines, **5**, the two grids will be geometrically related. If we now draw a shape such as a circle, in the first grid, and transfer each point of it to the second grid, we shall obtain an ellipse. We know quite instinctively that there is a relationship between the circle and the ellipse, but here it is shown in precise mathematical form. Likewise any other shape drawn in the first grid will be related to the one drawn in the second. If we draw the cannon bone of an ox in a grid as shown in **6**, and then draw two similar grids, **7**, **8**, and transfer the shape in the first grid, we shall arrive at the shapes of the cannon bones of the sheep and the giraffe. There is a definite mathematical relationship between these bones belonging to three different animals.

But not all relationships in nature are as straightforward as this. The two fishes in illustrations **10** and **11** are certainly related, but the grid of the second has been distorted, although the uprights are still parallel. It almost looks as though some unknown force had squeezed it together at one end and the development of the second fish over many thousands of years was changed. In this way it is possible to show the family

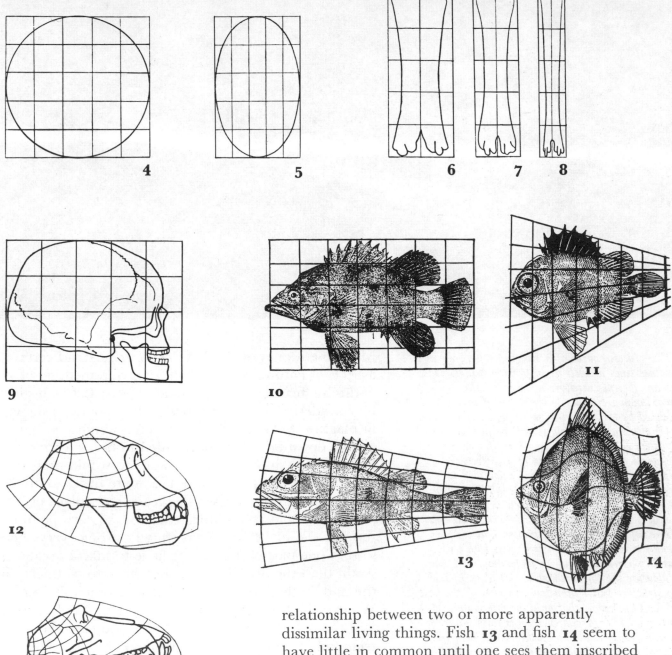

relationship between two or more apparently dissimilar living things. Fish **13** and fish **14** seem to have little in common until one sees them inscribed in their grids. A different kind of distortion from that of the previous grids is shown here, but it still falls into line with mathematical laws. Not only are the outlines of the two fishes related, but their skeletons also follow this distortion so that it would be possible for us to reconstruct the skeleton of the one from a knowledge of the skeleton of the other. Even the human skull, **9**, can be shown to be mathematically related to the skulls of the chimpanzee, **12**, and of the baboon, **15**.

1

*The graceful curve of a hanging rope, seen in clothes lines as well as suspension bridges, **1**, is an efficient curvature which gives the maximum resistance to the forces of tension caused by the weight of the rope, **2**. If we turn this curve upside down it will be just as efficient in compression, **3**. A reinforced concrete dome with a span of 130 feet, constructed in this form, and calculated to bear its own weight, would weigh only 300 tons. The cupola of St. Peter's in Rome, also with a span of 130 feet, weighs 10,000 tons. The difference is due to the fact that we have today a material which can resist both tension and compression, and we understand and can calculate the forces which are at work in such a structure better than the architects of the past did. This means that only the minimum of material is used, which accords with nature's methods. By applying mathematical principles to modern techniques and materials we could build a single vault to span the whole of St. Peter's Square, including the cupola of St. Peter's itself, **4**.*

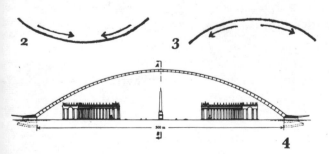

Mathematics not only allows us to understand certain aspects of nature, but can help to give something of nature's efficiency to man-made objects. Let us begin by considering a beam resting on two points as shown in diagram **5**. What happens when a weight, w, presses down on it? If you wanted to break a stick lying on two stones like the beam you would press it down in the middle, because it is more likely to break there than anywhere else. The least likely place of breaking would be at either end close to each point of support. To make our beam equally strong everywhere, so that one part of it does not have to take a greater strain than the rest, it would then have to be thicker in the middle than at the ends. But how much thicker? What is the best shape for such a beam? In order to find the best shape we could use the old method of trial and error. We could make many differently shaped beams, **6**, **7**, and try them all out till we found the most efficient one. A better way would be to calculate it. Underneath the diagram **7** you can see a formula which describes the effect which a load will have at any given point of the beam. Engineers call this effect the *bending moment*. If you insert values for w and l and varying x values for each point on the beam you can work out what the bending moment of a certain load at any point will be. You will find that the greatest bending moment occurs where x is half

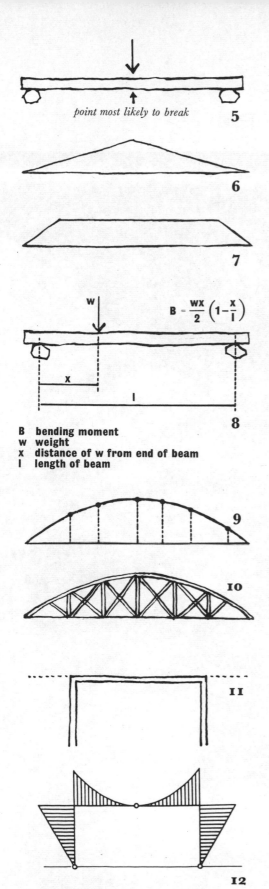

point most likely to break

5

6

7

$$B = \frac{wx}{2}\left(1 - \frac{x}{l}\right)$$

w

x

l

8

B   bending moment
w   weight
x   distance of w from end of beam
l   length of beam

9

10

11

12

of *l*, that is the middle of the beam, and least, that is nil, at the ends. This conforms with our first observations. If you now wanted to make your beam uniformly strong you would have to make it thickest where the bending moment is greatest; where the bending moment is less, the beam would have to be less thick, and so on. To draw the shape of the new beam you would have to convert your numbers representing the bending moments at each point into dimensions, as shown in diagram **9**. This is in fact a diagram of bending moments, but it is also the shape of the most efficient beam for these conditions. The new beam will be the diagram of moments given solid form, **10**. This curve can be shown to be a parabola. But if a horizontal beam is rigidly joined to two uprights at either end, **11**, as in many bridges, a different calculation would apply. In such a structure the beam is most likely to break at the ends and not in the middle. If you find this difficult to understand try and imagine a stick wedged between heavy stones at either end so that it cannot bend freely, **13**. Unlike the stick in diagram **5**, which is resting freely on two stones, it will break first where stones and stick meet, that is to say at the ends of that portion of the stick which we consider the beam. Picture **12** shows the diagram of bending moments of **11**. Translated into an actual concrete bridge, the shape would be something like that shown in **14**. In this way bridges reflect the conditions for which they are built; the diagram of their moments is nothing more than a mathematical explanation of their function.

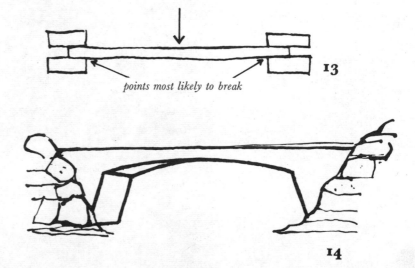

points most likely to break

13

14

15

The form of the bridge, **2**, with
the two projecting portions (called
cantilevers) is an approximation of
its diagram of bending moments, **1**,
adjusted to the needs of construction.
But such diagrams have to be
referred to in more than two
dimensions. When Nervi designed

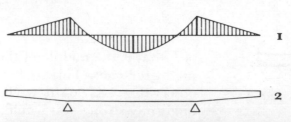

1

2

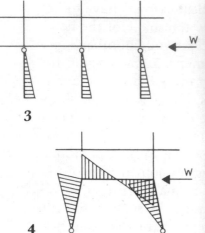

3

4

the UNESCO building in Paris he
calculated that the effect of wind
pressure on the supports on which
the whole building rests would
change considerably if the wind
veered by 90 degrees. These effects
can be expressed by diagrams, **3**, **4**,
which show that in one direction
the greatest stress will occur in the
upper part of each support, while
in the other direction the greatest
stress will be in the lower part.
He therefore designed supports to
withstand these stresses. You can
see from the diagram, **5**, and the
photograph, **6**, how cleverly he has
managed to do this. Similar
calculations are responsible for the
shape of the reinforced concrete
canopy in the background. These
interesting sculptural shapes are
wholly functional.

5   **6**

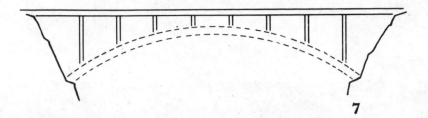

7

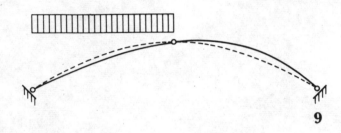

q

8

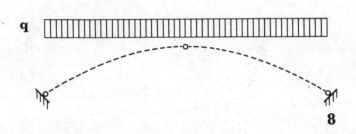

9

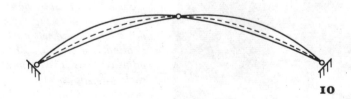

10

A bridge consists basically of two parts: the deck (continuation of the road) and the supporting arch, 7. For an evenly spread load, q, the best supporting arch would be a curve, 8, similar to that of the hanging rope, but turned upside down. But since bridges have to be able to withstand a great variety of uneven stresses this curve must obviously be modified. If a heavy load, such as a lorry, were to press on one side of the arch it would be distorted as shown in 9. If the lorry were to cross to the other side the distortion would be in the opposite direction. Diagram 10 shows the maximum distortion to which the arch is likely to be subjected in actual use. To build an efficient structure the arch must be made strongest where the distortion is greatest. The most practical shape would therefore be as shown in diagram 10, with hinges at both ends and in the middle to allow the arch to give. Diagram 11 shows how this basic shape of the arch can be combined with the deck to form one simple structure. Through this kind of creative thinking Robert Maillart, perhaps the greatest and most original bridge-builder of all time, designed and calculated his bridges. This is only one of a number of basic designs he devised for reinforced concrete bridges. The appearance of these bridges is not due to any visual ideas he may have had on how a bridge should look, but to the original structural thinking of a master engineer.

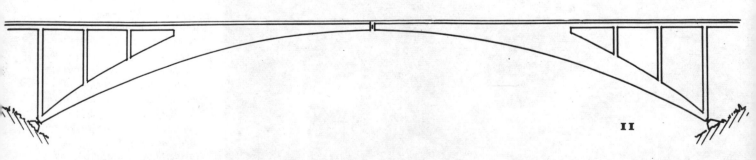

11

1

2 Even when Maillart built several bridges to the same basic idea he did not apply it blindly in all cases; he adjusted the shapes to meet each different set of conditions. That is why each bridge looks right for its own position. Notice how the shapes of the upright supports between deck and arch vary from bridge to bridge. The supports in picture **2**, like those of the other bridges, were calculated to provide firm yet flexible pillars. Their shapes remind one of human bodies straining to the task of holding up the deck of the bridge and we must remember that human bodies are constructed on similar principles. Looking at such bridges the functions of the three main components, deck, arch and supports, become

3

4

quite clear in one's mind. The designer fully understood them and expressed them in the most concise, economical and efficient form. We could compare their economy and efficiency to that of natural shapes. These bridges do not look out of place in the open country for which they were designed, leaping elegantly from bank to bank. The same cannot be said of the Saltash bridge, **4**. It does not have the visual meaning of a Maillart bridge because the structural principles are not clearly expressed.

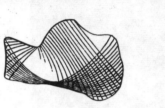

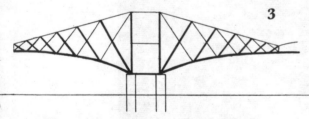

*The os calcis, **1**, and its stress diagram, **2***

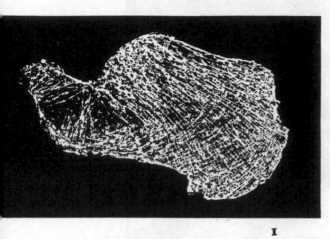

*The main structure of the Firth of Forth bridge consists of three double cantilevers. Each cantilever, **3**, has a number of parts which are designed to withstand compression (thick lines) and others which take tension (thin lines). The structure of the bridge is therefore expressed in visual terms and we can understand it by looking at it. A mammal's backbone acts in a similar way, compression members (bones) and tension members (ligaments) working together. Honesty of purpose in man-made shapes (not imitation of nature) bring them in line with nature's shapes.*

This principle is of course not new, nature has known it for millions of years. We have seen in Part Two that the thigh bone and the os calcis (a bone in the foot), **1**, **2**, are diagrams of forces in solid form, and even their interior structures conform to the diagrams. We may now consider the structures of whole animals in the same light. If we compare the basic structure of a quadruped, **4**, to a cantilevered bridge we shall see certain similarities. The diagram of bending moments of a horse's skeleton is shown in diagram **5**. As in the Firth of Forth bridge the greatest moment occurs immediately above each pillar (pair of legs) and one would expect the greatest structural strength in those places. You can see that the vertebrae from different parts of the horse's spine follow the diagram very closely. The vertebrae of the withers are higher than those of any other region. Animals in which neck and head do not form a cantilever from the forelegs have small vertebrae in the withers. The kangaroo with its upright posture is one such example. The iguanodon, **6**, is another. Animals with heavy, long tails have their strongest and highest vertebrae over their hind legs, for the same reason. In water the effect of gravity is neutralised and the idea of a cantilever loses its meaning. Mammals such as whales, **7**, and seals which live in water have therefore no high vertebrae over their withers.

The shapes of nature are not accidental. Rather they are adaptations to the needs of each situation. The skeletons of land mammals are basically cantilevered bridges, but they are more than that. When an animal moves about, many more forces and moments are added to the diagram which becomes exceedingly complicated. Furthermore we have only dealt with flat diagrams but in reality the forces act in many directions, so that a three-dimensional diagram would be necessary to understand these skeletons fully. But such diagrams would change with each second of the animal's life. It is wonderful to think that nature has made allowances for all this. Even our most sophisticated bridges are quite crude when compared to nature's structures.

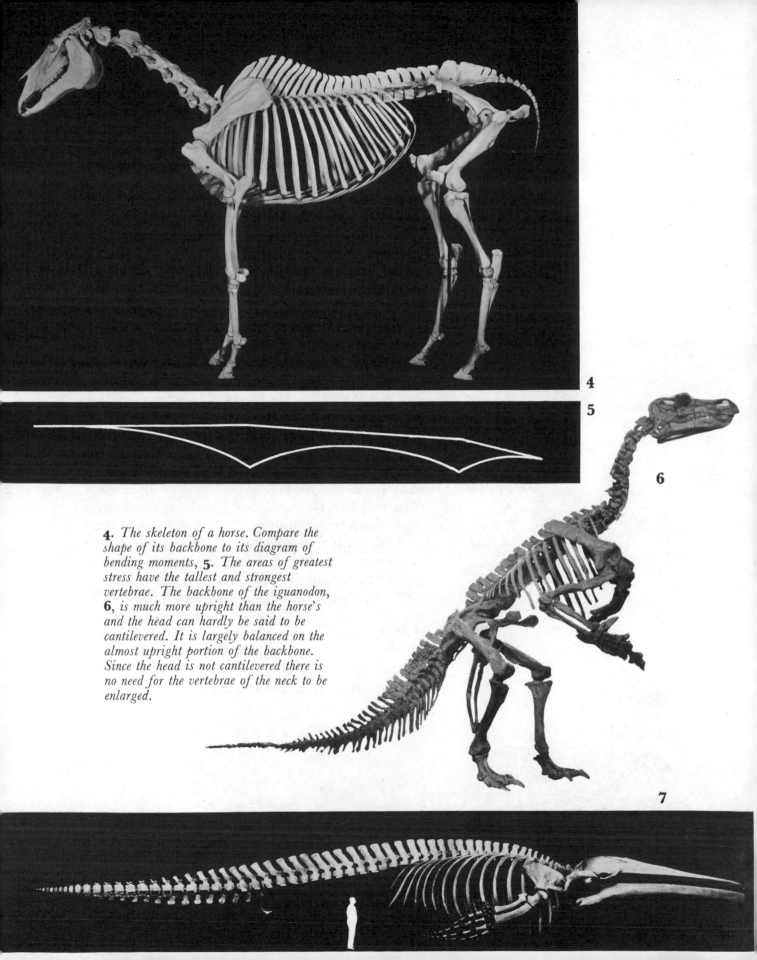

4

5

6

7

4. *The skeleton of a horse. Compare the shape of its backbone to its diagram of bending moments,* 5. *The areas of greatest stress have the tallest and strongest vertebrae. The backbone of the iguanodon,* 6, *is much more upright than the horse's and the head can hardly be said to be cantilevered. It is largely balanced on the almost upright portion of the backbone. Since the head is not cantilevered there is no need for the vertebrae of the neck to be enlarged.*

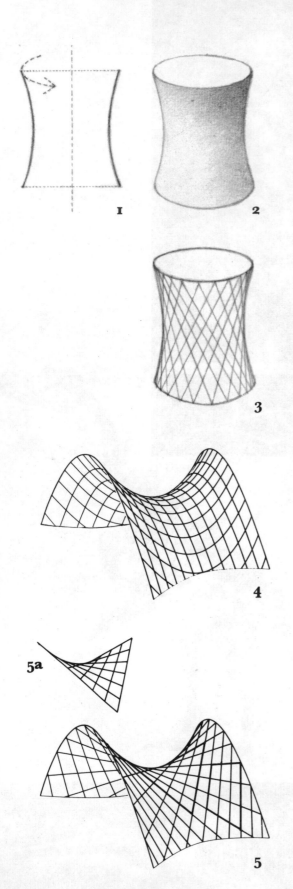

If you imagine a *hyperbola* rotating round an axis in a circular motion, the resultant shape will be as shown in diagram **2**. We can also produce this shape with a set of straight lines crossing another set of straight lines. This has advantages in reinforced concrete construction. A *rotational hyperboloid*, which is a double curved shape, can be reinforced with long straight rods which lie conveniently within this double curvature, **3**. This is why such shapes are well suited to reinforced concrete. Another mathematical shape of great interest to architects is the *hyperbolic paraboloid*. Felix Candela, a Mexican engineer, has developed this form with great success. It comes about when a parabola is moved in the path of another parabola in such a manner that it remains upright throughout, **4**. This gives a very interesting shape which again is composed of many *straight* lines lying within the curvatures, so that it does not pose any great problems of construction and reinforcement, **5**. In this drawing you can see that there are two intersecting *straight* lines at every point of the surface. It is difficult to realise that a complex shape can be built up entirely of *straight lines*.

Any portion of an HP (short for hyperbolic paraboloid) structure can be useful, such as the two drawn in thick lines in diagram **5**. The portion taken from the saddle, **5a**, is particularly useful for roof constructions, as shown in **6**. This mathematical shape, in spite of its apparent simplicity, can be fully understood only by walking round it, **7**. Any one view by itself will give us only part of its character. A building roofed with an HP construction seems to do away with the old distinction between walls and roof, **11**. The versatility of the HP construction is further shown by the many combinations to which it lends itself, **10**, **11**.

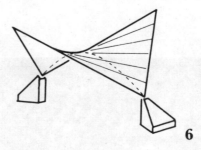

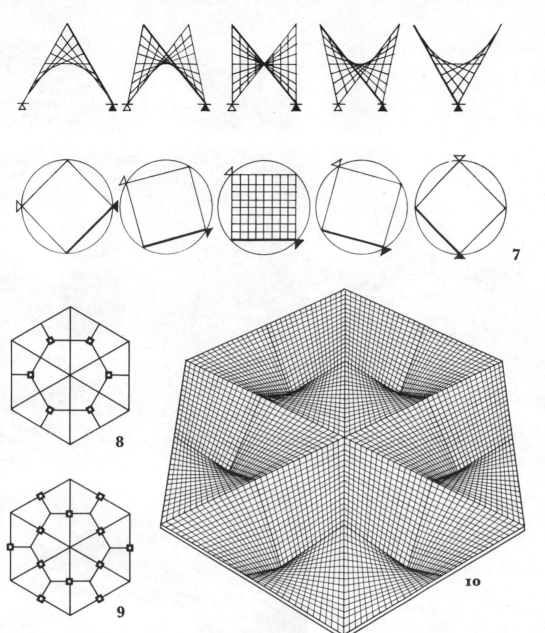

Like the pebble on page 102 of Part One, which did not unfold its true character until we had seen it from all possible angles, an HP cannot really be appreciated until one has walked round it and seen all its facets. **7** shows aspects of this simple yet fascinating shape. Under each drawing is a plan which indicates the changed position of the HP. It is a versatile shape which can be used in various combinations to form larger structures. Drawings **10** and **11** show two such combinations. **8** shows the ground plan of **10**, and **9** the ground plan of **11**. The small squares in **8** and **9** indicate the supporting columns required for each structure.

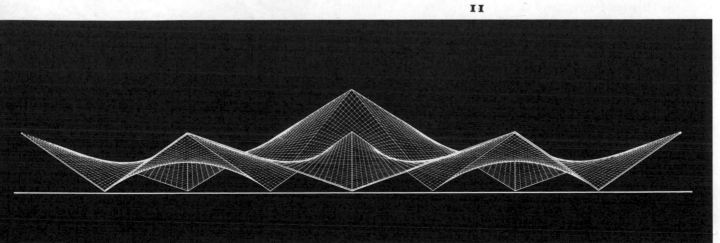

1

The roof of the Commonwealth Institute in London consists of a hyperbolic paraboloid with other curved surfaces added. Where the different curves of the roof meet a clerestory is formed. The whole complex roof structure has four supporting buttresses, two inside the building and two outside. This allowed the architect great freedom in designing the interior of the building, since, apart from the two interior buttresses, he had no pillars or load-bearing walls to reckon with. In fact by using this roof structure a span of 92 feet is achieved, which gives the whole building a remarkably spacious feeling.

Various views of the Commonwealth Institute
1. Aerial view showing the roof with clerestory. The sculptural quality of the external buttresses can be seen in 2. The interior view, 3, shows the enormous space spanned by the roof. 4 is a closer view, from the top gallery, of one of the two internal points of support. How gracefully the ribs describe the curvature!

2

3

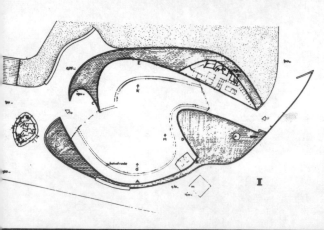

The Philips pavilion at the Brussels Exhibition in 1958, built by Le Corbusier, makes use of a number of different curved planes. The ground plan to be covered, **1**, was rather more irregular than that of the Commonwealth Institute, so that the structure also had to be more complicated. But you can see that it is largely made up of the straight lines of tension wires. The different aspects of this amazing structure have a quiet magnificence.

2 3

The shape of the Jaguar car, **4**, is calculated by the use of formulae. It is therefore unselfconscious and natural and expresses the car's function much better than the shapes of many cars which are meant to look fashionable or fast.
6 is a mathematical model of the kind used by mathematicians to visualise their formulae. It too has the beauty of natural shapes. Nobody could deny that the ship's screw, **5**, is also a pleasant shape; it is a calculated, that is to say, a mathematical one. There is no reason why such shapes should not be as pleasant as Maillart's bridges, or natural shapes such as fishes or trees.

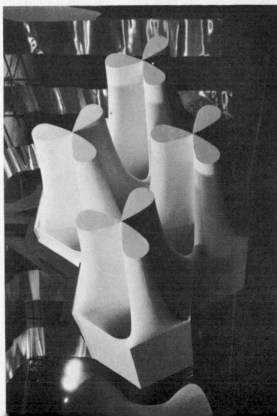

We have been looking at shapes which are clearly determined by mathematical calculations. More and more such shapes are entering our man-made world and in creating them we are approaching nature's methods more closely than was ever possible in the past.

The structure of the walnut (which has been compared to the dome of Hagia Sophia in Constantinople) or of a blade of grass, the shape of the seal and of birds, the construction of the most complicated animals down to the last tiny bone, all these examples of nature's ability to link shape to function can only be fully understood through mathematics.

In the past men strove to build in the most efficient way, but their knowledge of the forces of nature was incomplete, as was their knowledge of mathematics. Some great men could sense these forces and produce structures to withstand them by using their instinct and imagination. The invention of the Gothic pointed arch is one such instance, **2**; the invention of the parabolic girder bridge by Leonardo da Vinci another, **3**. Because they were efficient shapes they could dispense with a great deal of unnecessary material, and the key to their efficiency lay in their shape. They were designed as though the forces which acted upon them had been calculated.

Before the rise of modern technology there are only isolated examples of really efficient man-made shapes. Today however we can calculate the forces of nature and their likely effect, and we can design our shapes accordingly. In this way the man-made world has more and more in common with nature.

*1. The Pirelli building in Milan, designed by Gio Ponti (Part One, page 77, **5**) is calculated to withstand stresses similar to those a tree normally has to bear. It was not designed in imitation of a tree, but because similar principles are involved, the structures also have certain similarities.*

*The arrows in diagram **2** show the direction of the forces which Gothic structures are designed to withstand.*

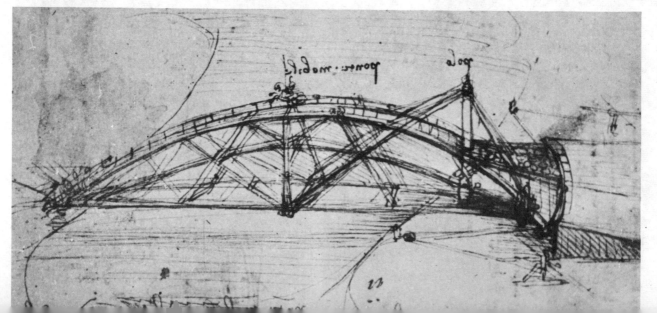

1

2

3

28

EXERCISES

1. Diagrams **4**, **5**, **6**, and **7** show how simple curvatures may be constructed by the use of straight lines drawn to connect certain points. You can see that the curvatures themselves are formed by straight lines and the closer together the lines are the more accurate and the smoother the curvature will be. Experiment with other curvatures.

2. In a similar way lines can be used to form three-dimensional shapes. But in order to construct such shapes we must use threads or thin wires instead of pencil lines. If you connect two pieces of wood as shown in diagram **9** the threads which connect them lie in the same flat plane. If you hold a piece of flat cardboard against them you can touch them all at the same time. But if you fix the upper lath with a long nail or dowel in such a way that it can be turned, you will be able to warp the plane in various degrees, **10**, **11**. The mathematical model, **8**, shows two such planes at the same time. They are both hyperbolic paraboloids.

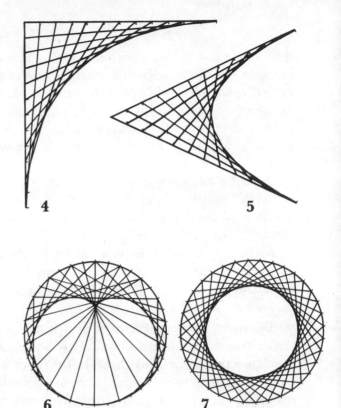

4

5

6

7

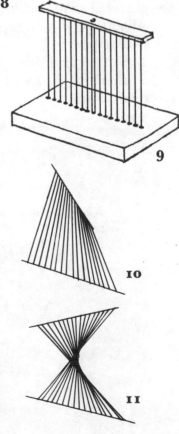

8

9

10

11

3. Diagram **1** shows another warped plane; it is quite straight on three sides and curved on the fourth. It is called a *conoid*. Architects often use it, chiefly for constructing roof lights in large buildings, **2**, **3**. Make a conoid or any other warped plane of your own imagination. Use threads or wires fastened to a framework of your own choice.

4. Make a drawing of your model.

5. Make another drawing of your model to show the warped plane described by the threads as a solid plane, as in drawing **2**, page 22.

6. Picture **4** shows how wire and thread may be used to make a variety of curved geometrical planes. Make experiments on these lines. Describe your best effort. Say what you like about it.

7. Picture **5** shows a piece of sculpture by the American artist Naum Gabo. It is made of pieces of transparent plastic and thread and describes a number of complicated planes which are subtly related to each other. Make experiments with any materials you choose which describe planes and their relationships in this way. Look at your model while you turn it slowly and watch the changing relationships between the various planes. From a sculptural point of view what is the advantage of a transparent structure like Gabo's over solid shapes?

8. Collect and draw a few natural objects in which mathematical aspects can be observed. Try to describe these aspects.

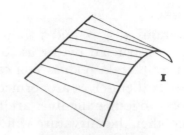

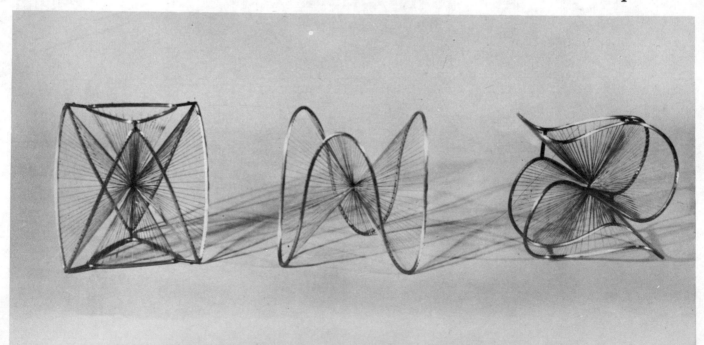

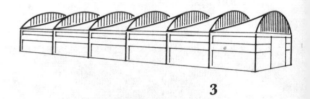

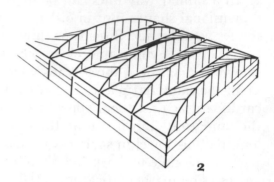

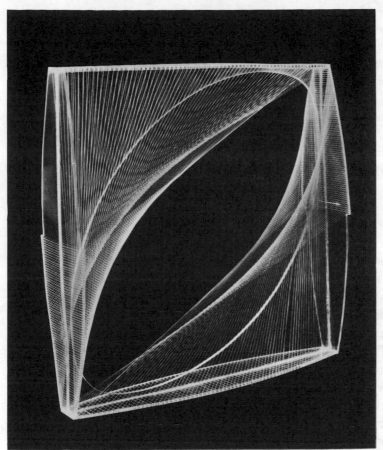

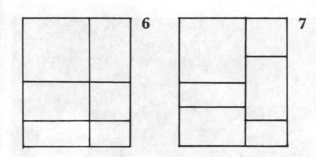

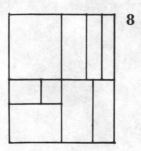

9. You have seen in this chapter (page 11, **8**) how a number of panels from the Modulor grid can be combined to form a large rectangular shape. In diagram **6** another set of panels is arranged in a rectangle, and re-arranged within the same shape, **7**. Re-arrange them once more. Diagram **8** shows how yet another set of panels may be used to fill the same shape. Choose another set of panels from the Modulor grid which will fill the same shape.

10. Le Corbusier has written a great deal about architecture and other subjects related to it. Here are two quotations from his writings. Can you explain what you think he meant? (a) 'The sap of mathematics has flowed through the veins of my work, both as an architect and painter; for music is always present within me.' (b) 'Proportion is the power which brings out the smile upon the face of things.'

11. Make drawings of any man-made things of which you think the mathematical aspects are particularly important or even obvious. Explain these aspects.

Design
for human beings

It is amusing to divide all man-made things into two categories: containers and extensions. For example, houses, coats and beds are containers; telescopes, lawn mowers and cars are extensions. Containers make life more comfortable for us; extensions extend the scope of our senses, our faculties, and our intelligences, and give us wider experience of the world. Such man-made things as come into contact with man, must, if they are to do their jobs efficiently, be designed to fit the human body at the point of contact. This has been recognised since the beginning of the tool-making era. The earliest ploughs were designed for use by human beings. They had to make provision for the fastening of the horse, they had to include a blade of the requisite shape, but as well as this the handle had to be of the correct height and the correct thickness for a human hand to grasp it.

The Norwegian scythe in this picture is over two hundred years old. The handle is carved in a twisted way to make its operation easier. It was not, however, always possible for the hard-pressed peasants of the past to spare time for such a long and intricate piece of work as this carving. Lack of time and skill explains why man-made objects were sometimes imperfectly adapted to human needs. Early chairs for example made little concession to the human form; to shape them to contain the human form in comfort was too difficult for the craftsmen of the period.

1

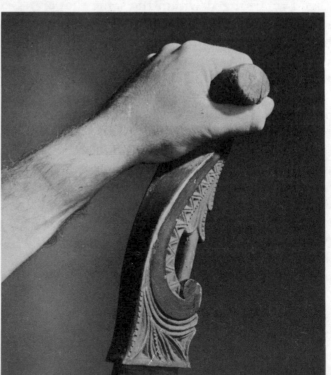

2

3 During the early Industrial Revolution engineers concentrated on the mechanical aspect of their machines and human beings had on the whole to fit in with the conditions imposed by the machines. As machines became more complicated and more difficult to operate their relation to the human body became the subject of careful study but only in the last few years has the application of this idea been at all widely made.

3. The controls of this locomotive were placed where the machinery demanded; human needs were hardly considered, whether in relation to the position of the controls or to their shapes. The machine became man's master. The controls of the lathe (shown in diagrammatic form, 4) bear little relation to the shape of a normal man. Only a freak human being could handle this machine easily, 5. Yet it was being produced as recently as 1961.

4

5

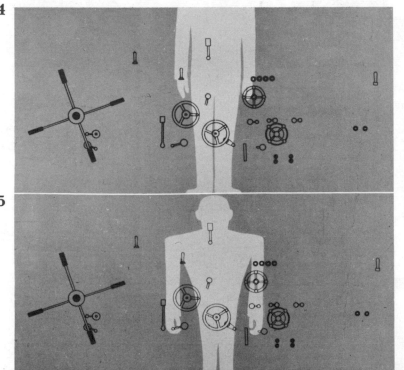

6

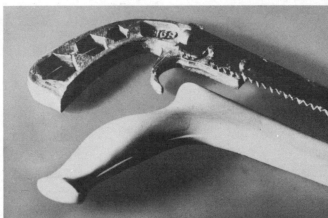

The old saw handle, 6, may have been cheap to produce but it also damaged the workers' hands. The improved version, based on a knowledge of human anatomy, is both more efficient and at the same time more beautiful to look at and pleasant to use.

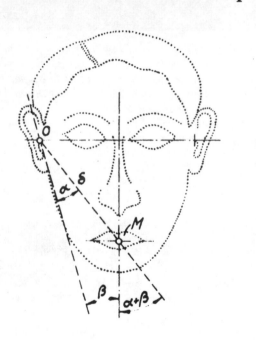

When Bell built his first telephone, **1**, it was not designed for human convenience. Looking at this picture, it is difficult to imagine how the instrument may be picked up or held in comfort. Over the years it was much improved mechanically, and the idea of its being used by human beings was undoubtedly taken into consideration, but only quite recently has there been designed a telephone in which the mechanical, production and human sides share equal attention. You can see that the instrument now assumes a shape suited to moulding in plastic, **8**. This makes it possible to reduce the number of components of the case. At the same time the shape of the human head has been considered in some detail. The design of this telephone seems to leave little to be desired from either the human or technical point of view.

I

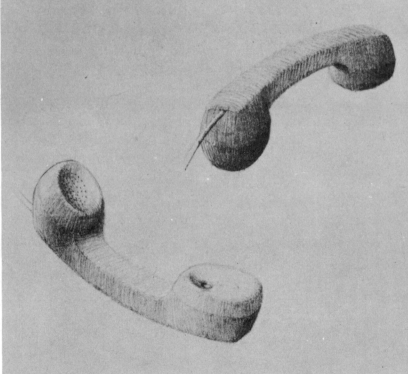

2   **3**

      4

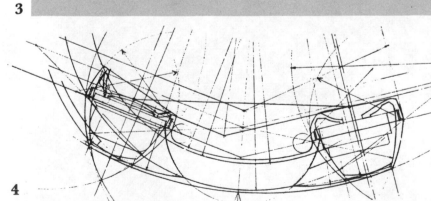

5

6

7

8

Measurements of the human head, **2**, are the first consideration in the designer's mind when he designs the receiver of a telephone. This information has to be fashioned into a shape which will also be suitable for mass-production in plastics. The first drawings show the application of these considerations, **3**. Most of the curvatures are reduced to simple arcs of circles, **4**. The main part of the instrument must also be suitable for the production methods employed; it must, moreover, act as a rest for the receiver and house all the mechanical and electrical components necessary, **7**, **9**. The final product, **8**, expresses the human use as well as its mechanical function. A new one-piece telephone incorporates all the parts in one shape, **5**, **6**. Again the use to which it is put is clearly expressed in the shape.

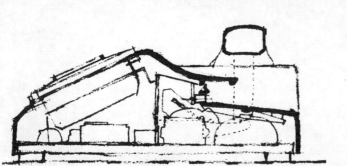

9

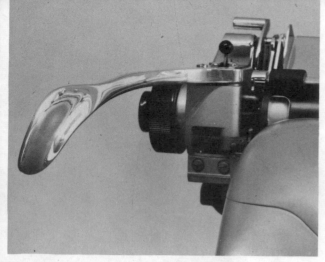

I

More and more objects are now designed from this point of view, as you can see in the pictures on these pages. All parts of the human anatomy which come into contact with man-made things are now measured, observed and considered, and the objects' points of contact shaped accordingly. We can refer to the design of machines as *mechanical design*. Let us give the name of *human design* to all design which increases the efficiency of man-made things from the human point of view. As you may imagine, this covers a very wide field indeed.

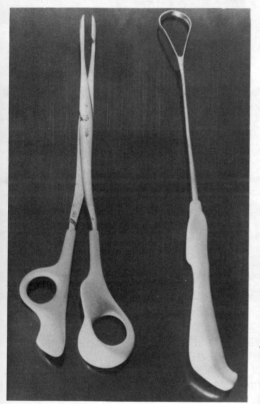

2   3

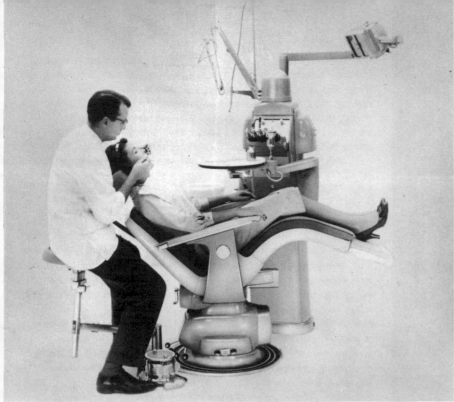

1. *The carriage return lever of a typewriter.* 2. *Surgical instruments.* 3. *The controls of a French car. How many different controls can you see in the picture?* 4. *A dentist's chair and equipment.* 5. *A camera. The release button is on top of one of the handles, where it can be easily reached by the thumb.* 6. *An industrial drill*

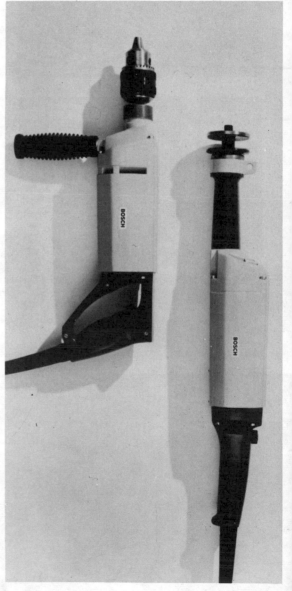

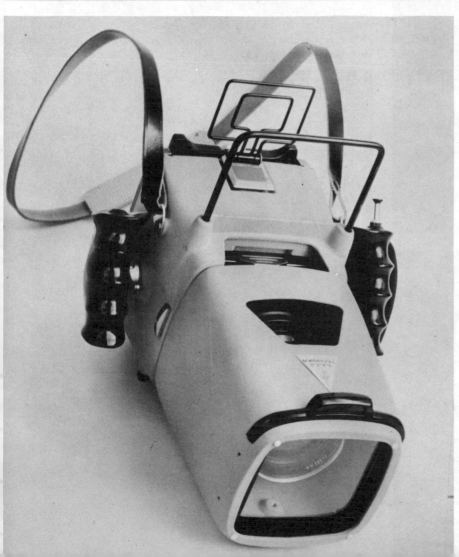

5 6

1

2

The old crane cab, **1**, was constructed on the most austere lines, the only concession to the human user being in the provision of windows. It must have been difficult to use. The operator, while turning the handles had to lean forward in order to see what he was doing, **2**. After a few hours' work this must have been an uncomfortable position, and people who have to work in uncomfortable circumstances are most liable to have accidents. The new crane cab, **3**, gives the operator excellent all round vision and he sits in a comfortable posture while operating the controls at his side. The French lorry cab, **4**, was designed on the same principles.

The controls of machines must be designed to make them efficient in human use, and this is particularly important in the case of knobs, pointers and dials. **5** and **6** show a set of knobs which not only express their function but are also easily distinguished from each other, even by touch in the dark. The neatly arranged knobs all of identical shape which one so often finds in modern cars are likely to cause mistakes and accidents. The design of pointers, especially on scientific apparatus, is also important. The pointer in **7** is badly designed; presumably it was intended to look streamlined and 'modern'. But the white line which indicates the position is not equally clear from all angles, so that 0 may be mistaken for 6, or 1 for 7. The pointers in **8** avoid this possibility of confusion. Many speedometer dials are almost illegible. Those shown in **9** and **11** seem to have been designed merely to look streamlined and 'modern-at-any-cost'. The one shown in **10** is better, though still difficult to read compared with an improved version, **12**.

3 4

5

7

8

6

9

10

11

12

The new telephone switchboard, **1**, shows how mechanical and human design can go hand in hand. The very conception of this switchboard is quite new. The harmonium-like form of traditional switchboards arose from the need to provide room for the weighted cords. But in this switchboard a new principle makes cords unnecessary. The designer did not need the old structure and used as his sole means of support a single column which could also contain the cable and several other items of equipment. This makes it possible for the switchboard operator to move her legs about freely and even cross them, a great advantage when many hours have to be spent in the same position. The wire baskets are for her personal belongings. The keys are arranged for ease of operation. Heights, reaching distances, angles of panels, and so on were determined by a thorough study of the operators' requirements. The colour and matt surface were chosen to avoid light reflection. The whole switchboard has a precise engineering form which at the same time meets the requirements of human design.

The lathe in picture **2** was an improvement on earlier models but further improvement was possible, as can be seen in picture **5**. Here the different parts of the machine are differentiated not only in form but also by the use of colour. At the same time the overall shape has been simplified. The close-up, **4**, shows how clearly all the controls are defined. This arrangement is not in any way haphazard, but the outcome of hard thinking about the use of the lathe. Even the numerical tables, **3**, have been designed with this in mind. In the nineteenth century many people thought that the only way out of the ugliness created by the Industrial Revolution was to cover up the machines or to disguise them. It never occurred to them to design them in the way that this lathe is designed.

3   **4**

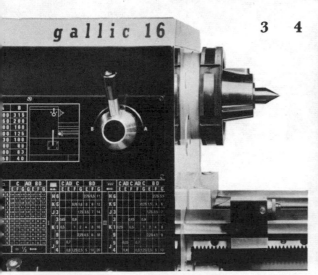

5

The ship's control room, **3**, tells the same story as the improved lathe. All the dials and warning lights can be seen from the central position, from which the controls can also be worked. Everything seems to be related, whilst in the older control room, **1**, each single item was considered in isolation and without relation to the rest. In the old signal box, **2**, the signalman must either remember to

3

4

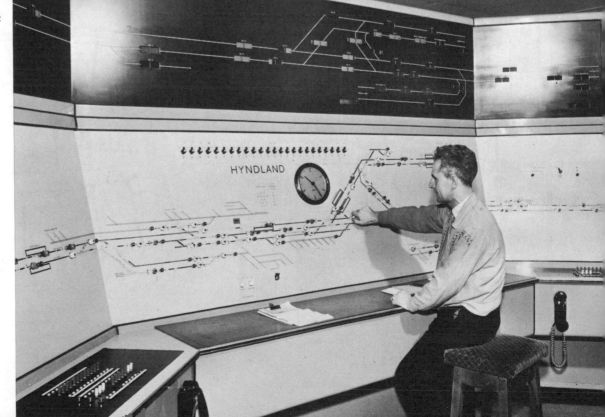

which point on the diagram each lever refers, or he must read the labels on each lever and refer them to the diagram – a hazardous procedure for so vital a job. In the new signal box, **4**, signals and points are operated by buttons on the diagram itself. This cuts out a number of actions and thought processes, makes operation more pleasant and accidents almost impossible.

HYNDLAND

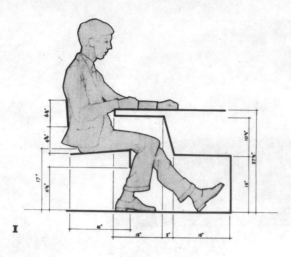

1

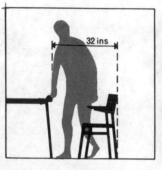

32 ins

26 ins

20 ins

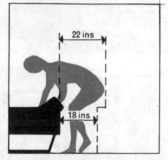

24 ins

20 ins

22 ins

18 ins

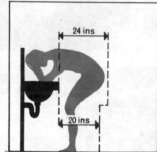

2

Furniture designed with little reference to the human body is inefficient. Diagram **1** shows some of the measurements which a designer of school furniture must bear in mind. Diagram **2** shows measurements which were the result of research into the movements of students. This information is as relevant to the arrangement of furniture as to its design, and this is especially important where both money and space are short, as is often the case with schools and colleges, student hostels and halls of residence. Diagram **3** shows a possible arrangement of furniture in a student's room so that the best use can be made of the smallest convenient space. **5.** A full-size model of a design for a student's room was set up so that it could be tested in actual daily use before the complete building was erected. You can see that the table is well sited in relation to the window, considering that a student's bedroom must also serve as a study. The shelves are movable, the settee converts into a bed to save space. The hall of residence of which this room forms a part consists of many such rooms, arranged as shown in diagram **4**. This shape has the advantage of providing room for a large staircase without wasting space at either end of the building. The corridors are curved; there are no long, straight, depressing passages such as are often found in institutions. The outside appearance of the residential block is shown in **6**. Its function is clearly revealed; it is a number of cells assembled into one building. The various buildings of the scheme will be arranged so as to make it possible to walk from any one block to any other under cover, **7**. Human design may start with door handles, but if it is to be really efficient it must go on to include whole buildings and even towns.

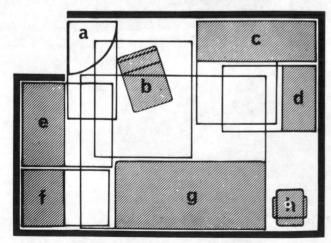

a *door*
b *easy chair*
c *writing table*
d *low cupboard*
e *wardrobe*
f *basin*
g *bed*
h *desk chair*

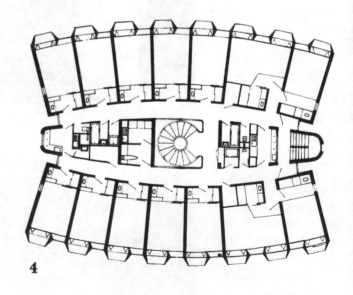

4

5

6 7

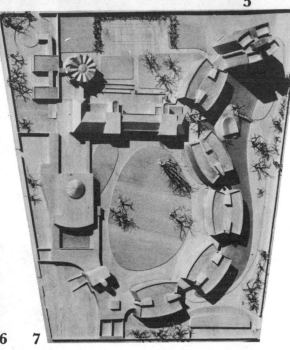

1

Because furniture and fittings are now mass-produced their design has become a matter of great importance, as each item now reaches a great number of people. The 'heart unit' is an innovation in building technique. These units, **1**, **2**, are supplied assembled and fully wired to be incorporated into houses while they are being built. This does not mean that all houses have to be alike, as many different arrangements (one is shown in **3**) are possible. Before such items are mass-produced and widely used we must make quite sure that they are in keeping with human needs. We must see to it that working surfaces are at the right level, and even adjustable, and that the various components are in a correct relationship. The same principles must be applied to prefabricated units used in new methods of building, **4**. Such units are necessary to keep the cost of building down but they will be of little use if they do not relate to human needs. They may be cheap and efficient from the mechanical point of view, but houses which are inefficient from the human angle have a habit of turning into slums before they are very old.

2 3

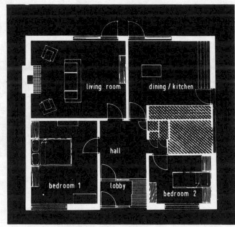

1. Dining Kitchen
2. Porch
3. Hall and staircase
4. Living room
5. Bedroom 1
6. W.C. and bathroom
7. Landing and cupboards
8. Bedroom 2
9. Bedroom 3

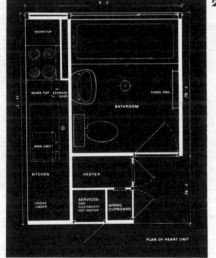

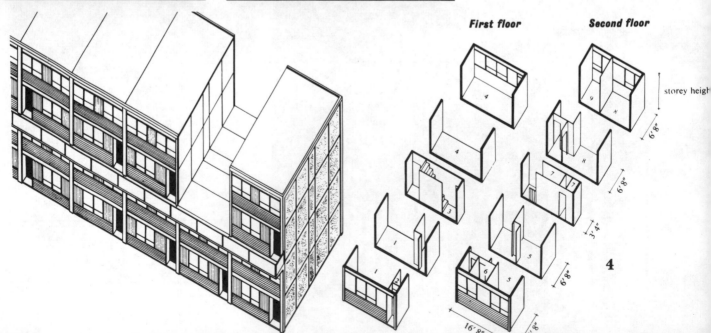

First floor   **Second floor**

storey height

4

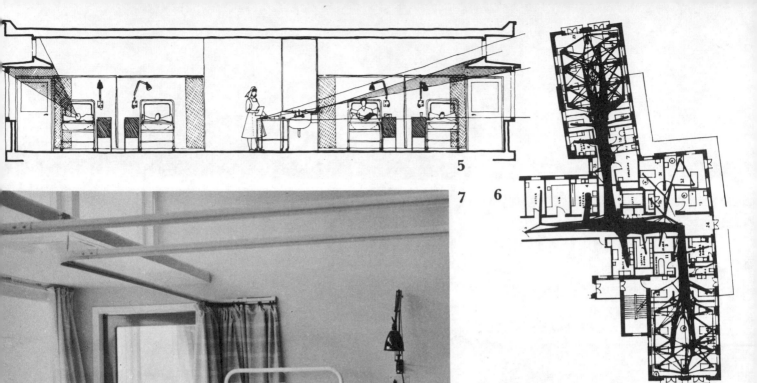

Hospitals used to be built in a 'style' but now their appearance is largely determined by the requirements of both staff and patients. In an old hospital building investigations were carried out into the movements of nurses during a day shift. These are shown by the black lines in diagram **6**. It was found, for example, that too much energy was wasted because nurses had to walk unnecessarily long distances between various places. Such diagrams have helped architects to design hospitals which are more efficient than older ones. The comfort of patients must be considered. For instance, patients lying near windows often suffer from glare, but shutters or curtains would darken the ward for those patients not lying so near to the windows. It has been found that a baffle with a clerestory above, **7**, can overcome this problem. Diagram **5** shows that although it eliminates glare from the sky (left), it allows plenty of light into the central part of the ward (right). This arrangement of windows has affected the appearance not only of the wards themselves, but of the whole building, **8**. Human design must affect the shapes of man-made things as much as mechanical design.

If public services, such as the railways, are to serve the community efficiently, all aspects of human needs, measurements, shapes, and habits must be considered. Such considerations obviously governed the design of the station shown in 1. The need for a covered drive resulted in a cantilever roof structure made of prefabricated parts. The diagram, 3, shows the movement of people using the station. Ticket offices, shops, doors were designed in relation to this diagram to make the operation of the station as smooth as possible, 2. Mechanical and human design here go hand in hand. The passengers' luggage trolleys, 5, are designed on the same principles. As in the case of the hospital, the staff's requirements have been carefully studied. The ticket office, 6, as it existed before the old station was replaced by the new, was unpleasant and frustrating to work in. In what way is the new ticket office, on the left in picture 2, or the one in picture 4 (from another station) better to work in? Do you think they are also better from the passengers' point of view?

3 4

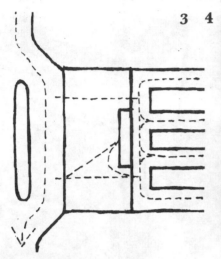

5 6

1 2

Railway carriages are now being designed to fit human needs better than ever before. As in the structure of the station, human design has been expressed in shapes relevant to modern materials. The seats are fibreglass shells, **2**; their shape is a result of a thorough study of the human body, **3**. Magazine racks and collapsible tables are built in, **2**. Because of the shell-like structure there is luggage space under the seats, **2**. Lights are built into the luggage racks. A new door which partly pivots and partly slides back into the carriage has made possible a wide opening and a wide lobby. The advantages of the new door, **4**, over the old, **5**, are obvious. Efficiency and human design do not end with the trains. New letter forms for use on train indicators have been devised. The thickness and shape of these letters are carefully related so as to make them more legible when illuminated.

4

5

6

7

8

9

Enquiries

Compare the new letters, **6**, left, to the old, **6**, right; the difference is even greater when seen from a distance, **7**. For station signs another set of letters has been designed, but as legibility also depends on letter-spacing a system has been worked out, **8**, which enables railwaymen with no experience of lettering to compose signs, such as **9**. You will see that not all the letters are equally spaced apart, but the general impression is one of evenness.

Human design is now probably more important than ever before. The machines and utensils we handle are often much more complicated than those of the past, and they must be made simple enough for people of average intelligence to control them. Mistakes can now have far more serious consequences than a few generations ago. In addition to this, life has become more harassing. Most of us travel farther to work and in greater discomfort than our parents did. If we drive a car we are under a constant strain and are often frustrated in our movements. In towns, even walking about, or getting a meal has become a strain. At the same time most people find their work more exacting and they require more relaxation in their leisure hours. Human design will therefore have an ever increasing role to play in the future, if conditions are not to become intolerable for most people. Perhaps one of the greatest problems of human design will be to find a way of eliminating the causes of strain at their source. When we hear the word design we normally think of the design of objects we can handle, such as pans, chairs, scooters. But a town too is something which has to be designed. We know that the design of everyday objects must change as the materials used for them and the functions they perform change, but we do not normally consider towns in this way. Even though we do not realise it, the design of the town in which we live has probably a greater effect on us than all the pots and pans and chairs which are often so carefully designed. What is a town if not a large human design? And how many towns are suited to the conditions of work and leisure as they exist today? We modernise our old-fashioned houses, but it is more difficult to fit our old-fashioned towns for life in the twentieth century and to make them into places where human beings can live happy and relaxed lives. Research of the kind which makes possible human design for machines and furniture is needed before we can do anything to re-shape our towns effectively. For instance, it is obvious from every one's experience that motor traffic and pedestrians do not mix, but little has yet been done to separate them. This is only one of many problems which will have to be solved if our towns are to become again the pleasant places they once were.

I

2

Then there is the purely visual aspect. Our industrial towns are often ugly because they were not designed with the needs of human beings in mind. This typical street corner, **3**, in an English town contains many different items each of which was installed without regard to the unity of the whole design. The shabbiness and sordidness of the town is a direct result of this haphazard growth. Quite apart from the lack of planning in the layout of this street corner, the individual shapes of the street furniture are without any feeling for their function, the materials they are made of, the methods of manufacture, and their effect on people. How can people be proud of their towns and care for their appearance with the evidence of so much lack of understanding all round them?

3

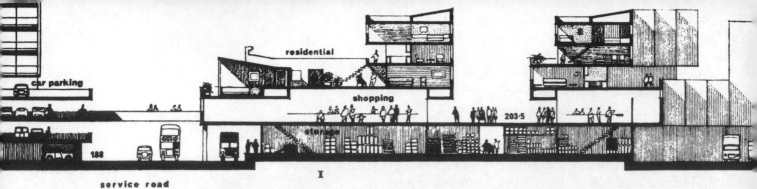

car parking

residential

shopping

203·5

188

service road

I

2

The new towns which are now being built in many parts of the country incorporate all that is known about human design on the very largest and smallest scales. Instead of copying the layout of older towns which suited different conditions our new towns will fit human needs as they exist now. Long-distance traffic, local traffic, cyclists and pedestrians will be kept separate in the streets of the replanned Andover. The service roads from which vans and lorries pull into loading bays are to be closed to pedestrians, **1**. Storage space for shops is provided at road level. Shoppers' cars can be parked at high level car parks. Pedestrians approach the pedestrian deck by bridges over the road. In picture **2**, which shows a model of this proposed new town centre, you can see the service road running diagonally from the top left corner towards the centre; the bridges over it are also visible. Picture **1** is a section running at right angles to the road towards the church in the top right-hand corner. **3** and **5** show how these areas will probably look. New ideas are also applied to residential areas of new towns. Diagram **4** shows a part of the new

3

4

5

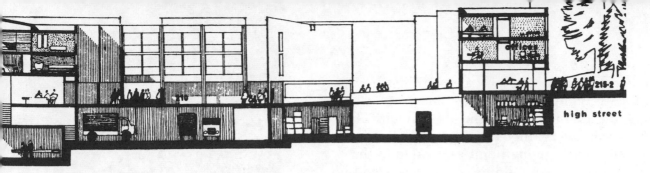

high street

town at Haverhill. The solid black lines indicate roads for motor vehicles, including service roads and parking areas, the dotted lines are footpaths. You can see that pedestrians are kept away from motor traffic as efficiently as in the town centre of Andover. The footpaths run between the central service roads without ever crossing them, while the ring road has several underpasses to enable pedestrians to cross into neighbouring areas. It will be possible to walk from one end of the town to the other without ever crossing a road. Children will be able to go to school in absolute safety; the strain on drivers will also be lessened. This is human design on a very high level, but to complete the picture we must also attend to the details. The telephone kiosk, **6**, is one such detail and in this case the design is also of a high order. Look for instance at the door handle and compare its efficiency with one on the older type of kiosk, **8**. Not only is it easier to open a heavy door with a handle of this construction, but through its size and shape it gives one a

definite visual idea of the way in which the door opens. The camouflaged, recessed finger grip of the older one hides its function. The telephone itself is designed for easy operation, again in terms of modern materials and production methods, **7**. The figures and letters are outside the dial where they are more easily seen. The directories can be swivelled into an upright position for use, when turned down they make a convenient writing surface. Everything inside the box is arranged to give more space, although the overall measurements are the same as the older one. Apart from being more efficient in use the telephone kiosk and receiver are more pleasant to look at. The quality of a town is determined not only by the overall pattern, **1, 2, 3** and **4**, but also by the attention to details within the master plan and the relationships between the details. Everything from architecture to the design of telephone receivers must express the same attitude: a desire to make the town serve the needs of each human being and of the whole community.

6

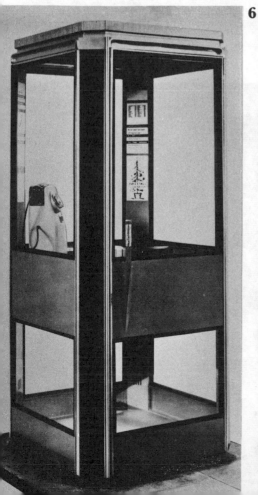

7 8

We have seen that man can look at the things he makes from two points of view: the purely mechanical and mathematical, and the human. The two need not conflict; rather they should be complementary, each giving point and value to the other. The world we are building for ourselves will not be fit for human beings unless we build it with these two points of view in mind. Yet we continue to produce uncomfortable chairs, almost illegible speedometer dials, houses which do not fit our needs and are difficult to run, whole neighbourhoods which are as irrelevant to twentieth century conditions as castles and moats and which, by their inefficiency, cast a blight on the development of human life. Look at pictures **1** to **7** carefully and decide why these objects were made in these shapes and whether the principles we have discussed in the last two chapters were taken into account by the makers. Do you think the objects show that some of our designing is still moving in the wrong direction? Unless the importance of human design is fully understood, human beings will exist in an environment more and more dominated by the machine. Human design is a form of respect for human life.

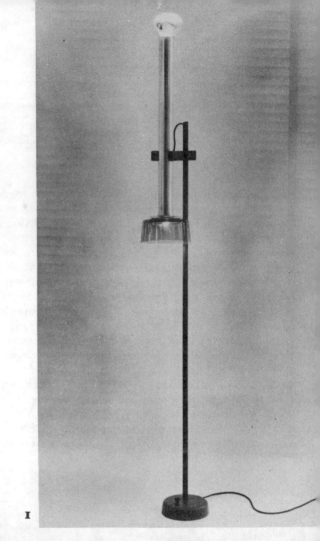

1

2

3

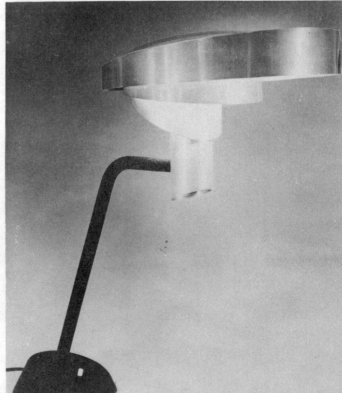

4

5

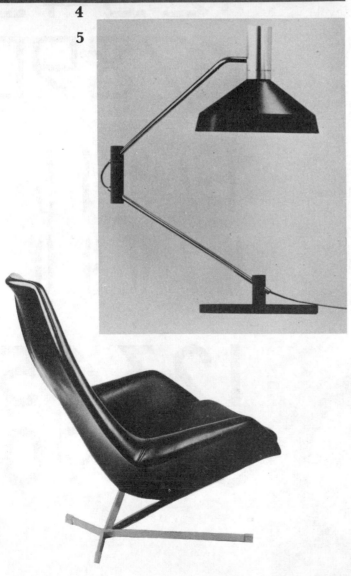

The three items on page 56 look modern but are they really well designed? The chair, **2**, speaks for itself: this is no place for tired limbs. The designer wanted to produce a chair which looks interesting and different from other chairs. What do you think made him want to do this? The standard lamp, **1**, attempts to look machine-like and efficient but succeeds only in looking pretentious. The effect could have been achieved by simpler means. Because of its exaggerated shape and the fact that it is top heavy it is easily knocked over. A larger foot would presumably have destroyed the slender and delicate appearance its designer intended for it. The table lamp, **3**, is likewise pretentious and unnecessarily complicated. Compare these lamps with **4** and **5**. How modestly **4** seems to perform its duty, but it does so with greater success and charm than either **1** or **3**. **5** may have a superficial resemblance to **1** but is in reality a well-balanced, adjustable lamp which works with the minimum of fuss. The designers of the chairs, **6** and **7**, related materials and construction to human needs. The elegant angles of **7** are determined by the need, to give firmness and balance to the chair and comfort to the user. They are essential to the structure and not added as an embellishment. When folded the two parts of the chair fit neatly into each other. **6** is a fibreglass shell, upholstered and balanced on a metal structure. The essential difference between the objects shown opposite and those on this page is one of human design. The objects on this page are designed to work for human beings. The objects opposite try to tell us something about themselves. And like all people who talk too much about themselves they grow rather boring.

6   7

1

EXERCISES

1. Explain what aspects of the light switch, **1**, are the result of human design.

2. Examine a number of tools and machines, for instance a pair of pliers, a sewing machine, a bicycle, a gas cooker, from the point of view of human design. Illustrate your answers by drawings if necessary.

3. Examine a number of pieces of furniture in the same way.

4. Examine picture **4**, page 43. Can you find anything to criticise?

5. Compare the older dial, **5**, with the improved version, **6**, and describe in what ways **6** is better than **5**. Can you find anything wrong with **6**?

6. Examine a number of dials and clock faces from the point of view of human design.

7. Examine the three sets of figures, **2**, **3**, and **4**, taken from dials found on various appliances, and explain which you think are most suitable for use on dials. Say why you think the others are unsuitable.

8. Look at picture **3**, page 41, and picture **9**, page 51, and explain what part human design plays in each.

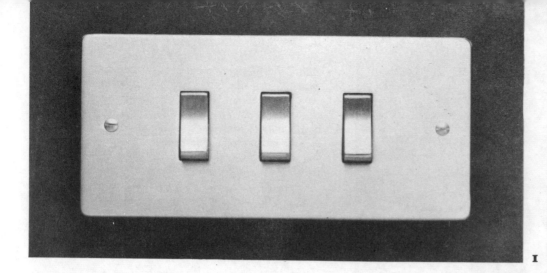

2

3

4

5   6

Visual communications

Communications between human beings play a very important part in twentieth-century life. If one buys a propelling pencil or a frying pan or a racing car there is sure to be an instruction leaflet or instruction book to go with it. More people than ever before read newspapers and books, listen to the radio, and watch television; every year more forms have to be filled in for a variety of purposes; signs and directions confront us wherever we go. All these, and many more, are means of communication. We seem to have a great deal to say to each other in the twentieth century. Many, if not most, of these means of communication are in visual form; printed time tables, road signs, instruction books, for example. In the last chapter we have already seen some methods of visual communication: for instance, the tables of figures on the lathe on page 41; the dials on page 43; even the panel on the telephone switchboard on page 40. If we look at other examples of visual communications we soon begin to realise that they are in every way a part of human design.

Some of the biggest and perhaps most important visual communications are to be found in streets and alongside roads. Let us consider the signs in these pictures in the same way as other examples of human design. In what way do they help us? Is their message put over efficiently? Here we must again refer to the manner in which we use them. The cluster of signs, **1**, would be quite adequate for the leisurely days of the stage coach, but does it work in these days of fast-moving motor transport? The road sign shown in picture, **2**, by the size and clarity of its layout, is obviously designed for the needs of our times. The older sign, **1**, can give rise to accidents.

1

2

The road sign, **2**, tells the driver what to expect. There are two blind side alleys which lead nowhere; the road ahead leads to Colnbrook and Staines; a right turn followed by a left turn will take the driver on to the Slough road; a turn of 180 degrees followed by a left turn leads to West Drayton. Road numbers are also given, in a different colour for clarity. Most of this road sign gives a great deal of very precise information at a glance. It may be understood in a fraction of the time it has taken you to read this caption. The cluster of signs, **1**, gives its information haltingly, like someone not sure of his grammar, so that you have to reflect before you can be sure of the message.

In a densely populated town, road signs must be related to other signs, and, like the street furniture, to the whole picture of the street. Road signs, erected at random, often duplicating each other, are not only a danger to traffic but a blot on the landscape Surely at a time when so many signs are necessary it would be wise to keep them to an essential minimum? What is one to think of a street where a battery of signs of every description assault the passers by? The very lettering, with its lack of planning, breeds confusion and a chaotic pattern. Where has our harmonious human pattern got to? What point is there in designing buildings which create a good pattern when it can be overlaid and even destroyed by the signs of the individual shopkeepers and the various authorities who need to erect signs?

If all the good work of other designers is not to be completely undone, we must pay attention to visual communications. The wonderful design of the lathe on page 41 would be made less efficient by a badly designed table of figures; a well-designed street can be marred by bad shop and street signs. We must relate our street signs to the street furniture and to the architecture. In the past when people were more closely bound to their town and understood its character and had a feeling for harmonious patterns, streets were never allowed to look like **1** and **7**. Let us hope we shall have the sense to avoid this sort of ugliness in the towns and neighbourhoods which are being built now.

2 **3**

4

5

The shop signs, **2, 3, 4,** are almost illegible. Because they compete for attention they also create disharmony. Official signs are often not much better. The signs in **5** are badly designed as bearers of information, and made still less efficient by bad positioning. Most of the signs you see on these two pages will make even the most beautiful buildings and streets look squalid.

7

1 TURN LEFT

2 KEEP LEFT

3 DOUBLE BEND

4 HALT AT MAJOR ROAD AHEAD

5

6

7

8

9 STOP

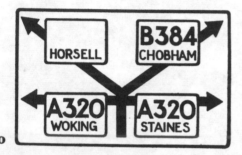

10 HORSELL · B384 CHOBHAM · A320 WOKING · A320 STAINES

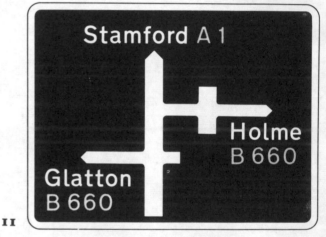

11 Stamford A 1 · Holme B 660 · Glatton B 660

The old road signs, **1** to **4**, have many faults. They are difficult to take in, especially at speed. Because they are badly put together they do not work well, like a badly contrived machine. Too much of their message is in the form of lettering, and is not as easily absorbed as a message conveyed by visual symbols, such as **5**, which may be taken as typical of the modern language of road signs. It makes efficient use of an abstract symbol to convey the sudden need for care and attention. It expresses the abstract idea of a warning in visual terms. Foreigners who cannot understand English cannot follow the directions in **1** to **4**. The letters are badly designed and the words badly placed. The new signs, **6** to **9**, convey the same messages as their predecessors, **1** to **4**, but they are more efficient. Can you say

why? The new signs have a stronger family resemblance and can be recognised as road signs much more quickly. **11** has every appearance of an efficient mechanism, which indeed it is. Even the colours have been applied with a view to efficient communication. The shape of the old sign, **10**, is arbitrary. We could compare the signs shown in **10** and **11** to the two dials, page 58, or the two signal boxes, pages 42 – 43, or the crane cabs, page 38.

POST OFFICE

NO WAITING 8AM-6.30PM
NO LOADING OR UNLOADING 12 NOON-2.30 PM

Longbridge Hayes · Chesterton · Red Street · QUEUE OTHER SIDE

15   16

17
18

19

Here are some well-designed shop signs. In each case the sign is related to the shop itself and not arbitrarily added. The shops are designed to display their wares and to serve us, not to shout at us. Such honesty and sympathy with the requirements of the community are needed if we are to have civilised towns. The official signs, **12**, **13**, **14**, have enough character to show at a glance to which public service they belong and what they are about. They are also well-designed, that is to say, they are easy to read and well composed within their shapes. These signs and the shop signs, **15**, **16**, **17**, **18**, **19**, if related to each other with skill and imagination, should add to the quality of a town or street. The signs on pages 60 and 61 have the opposite effect.

Acharius.dicitur a macha quod est in
genium a ares virtus vel dicitur a macha
quod est percussio a rio magister fuit
enim ingeniosus contra demonis falla/
ciam virtuosus quintum ad vitas percussio
in donatione corporis magister in regi/
mine prelationis vel macharius io est
beatus.

Macharius
abbas de/
scendit de
syti a intuit dormire
in monumento vbi
sepulta erant corpa
paganoz a extraxit
vnu corp? s6 caput
suu tanq pulmariu
Demones aut volé/
tes eu terre vocabat
q̃si vnam mulierem
dicentes· surge veni
nobiscu ad balneuz
a ali demon sub ipo
tanq ex mortuo illo
dicebat peregrinum
quenda habeo sup me a no possu venire. Ille aut no expauit
ß tñdebat corp? illud dicens surge a vade si potes a audietes
demones fugierunt voce magna clamates vicisti nos dñe. Dú
aliqñ abbas machariz a palude ad cella sua pteriret occurrit
ei dyabolus cu falce melsoria a volens eum cu falce pcuttere
non potuit. Et dixit ei multa violentia pacior a te machari qa
no possu preualere aduersu te. Ecce eni quicqd tu facis a ego
facio ieiunas tu a ego penitus non comedo vigilas tu a ego
modo non dormio. Vnu est solummo in q me supas a dixit
abbas qd est illud. Cui ille humilitas tua p qua no preualeo
aduersu te. Dú teptacoes ipm iuuené molestarent surgens a
magnu saccu arene humeris suis imponens diebz multis sic
p desertu ibat qué theosebi? inueniés dixit· abba cur tin on?
portas Et ille vexo vexaté me. Abbas machariz vidit sathana
transeunté in hitu bois a habenté vestimentu lineu laceratuz
et p via foramia dependebat ampulle a dixit ei. Quo vadis a

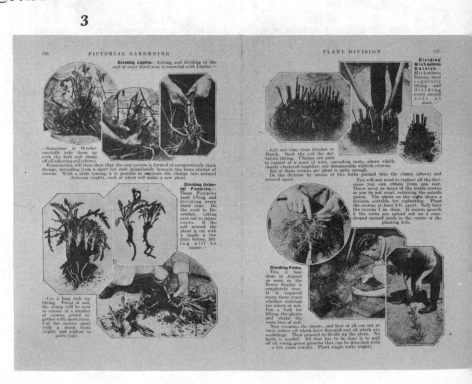

EN france aura auant le temps de paine et
de terriblete trois grans arbzes qui flozstrōt
et auront fueilles Mais point ne pozteront
de fruict qui viengne a meurisson. et de leurs raci
nes naistront aultres trois arbzes qui ne pozteront
ne fleuzs ne fueilles. mais de eulx naistrōt fruictz
et des racines deur naistra vng cō q souslzaira et
destruira moult de la substance des trops arbzes

1   **2**

3

We have seen how early craftsmen, because
they were in sympathy with their materials,
produced patterns and shapes which were
both practical and harmonious. This also
applies to printing. In these two specimens
of early printing, **1, 2,** we can see what
difficulties these printers had to overcome,
because of the crudeness of their equipment.
The letters are not as even and clear as we
would expect them to be today, nor are
they perfectly aligned. But in spite of this
lack of mechanical perfection there is a
harmony between the letters themselves and
also between type and pictures. If you were
to interchange the pictures they would –
apart from their size – look out of place.
The craftsmen who cut these pictures on
wood had a profound understanding of the
design of a book such as we rarely find
today. How do you think the gardening
book, **3,** compares with **1** and **2**?

Not all visual communications are as large as street signs. Books, which are among the oldest visual communications, carry information of all kinds. A book which is not easy to read is not an efficient book. Few people realise how much thought must go into a well-designed book, where, as in all well-designed things, there must be a balanced relationship between the various elements. The choice of type is partly determined by the subject matter of the book, partly by the sort of people who are expected to read it, partly by the kind of paper to be used. The relationship between the margins and the type area must also balance well. Even the design of such a familiar object as a book requires a great deal of thought and understanding.

Book illustrations are an important part of the design and must be carefully related to the whole. The diagrams, photographs, and type in these examples, **4**, **5**, work particularly well together. Not only do they help to clarify the text but they also give the book a character in keeping with its subject matter. Lack of relationship between text and illustrations can spoil a book, just as lack of planning can spoil a street.

4

Pages from two well-designed books. Both are effective in their own way as well as pleasant to look at and to use.

5

Formerly nature was in balance; or, to be more precise, every animal and vegetable species lived in equilibrium with its environment. We must never forget that achieving this equilibrium was a harsh process. But neither let us forget that it once did exist and that it was distroyed.

1

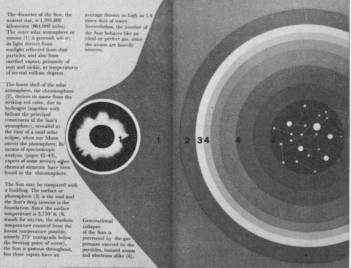

The diameter of the Sun, the nearest star, is 1,391,000 kilometers (864,000 miles). The outer solar atmosphere or corona (1) is greenish white; its light derives from sunlight reflected from dust particles, and also from rarefied vapors, primarily of iron and nickle, at temperatures of several million degrees.

The lower shell of the solar atmosphere, the chromosphere (2), derives its name from the striking red color, due to hydrogen (together with helium the principal constituent of the Sun's atmosphere), revealed at the time of a total solar eclipse, when our Moon covers the photosphere. By means of spectroscopic analysis (pages 42–43), vapors of some seventy other chemical elements have been found in the chromosphere.

The Sun may be compared with a building. The surface or photosphere (3) is the roof and the Sun's deep interior is the foundation. Since the surface temperature is 5,750°K (K stands for KELVIN, the absolute temperature counted from the lowest temperature possible, namely 273° centigrade below the freezing point of water), the Sun is gaseous throughout, but these vapors have an average density as high as 1.4 times that of water. Nevertheless, the interior of the Sun behaves like an ideal or perfect gas, since the atoms are heavily IONIZED.

Gravitational collapse of the Sun is prevented by the gas pressure exerted by the particles, ionized atoms and electrons alike (4).

2

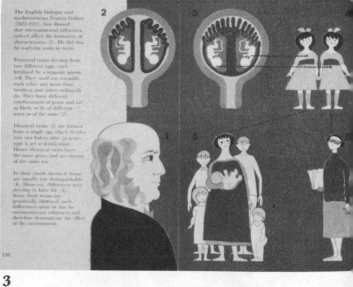

The English biologist and mathematician Francis Galton (1822–1911), first showed that environmental influences indeed affect the formation of characteristics (1). He did this by studying traits in twins.

Fraternal twins develop from two different eggs, each fertilized by a separate sperm cell. They need not resemble each other any more than brothers and sisters ordinarily do. They have different combinations of genes and are as likely to be of different sexes as of the same (2).

Identical twins (3) are formed from a single egg which divides into two halves after its genotype is set at fertilization. Hence identical twins have the same genes and are always of the same sex.

In their youth identical twins are usually not distinguishable (4). However, differences may develop in later life (5). Since these twins are genetically identical, such differences must be due to environmental influences and therefore demonstrate the effect of the environment.

3

Pages from three illustrated paperbacks
The titles are: **1**, *'Population Explosion',*
2, *'Space'*, **3**, *'Genetics'. Do you think the*
illustrations are useful?

Book cover and jacket designs combine in many ways the function of poster and illustration. These four designs state in visual terms what the books are about. Had they all been printed in the same type on white paper their different messages would not have been so clear to us: the character of each book would not have been expressed. Do you think it is important that the outside of a book should express its character? **6** is particularly interesting. It shows how the first inarticulate sounds of savages have gradually settled into definite patterns which eventually became our language. The designer described something which it is very difficult to show in a picture. He has used very simple means – printing type – to achieve his ends. He has succeeded brilliantly, giving us something like a diagram of the book.

4

5 6

7

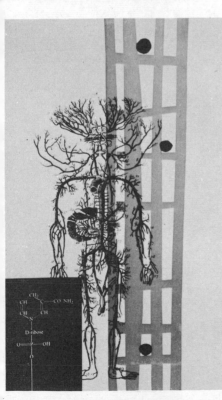

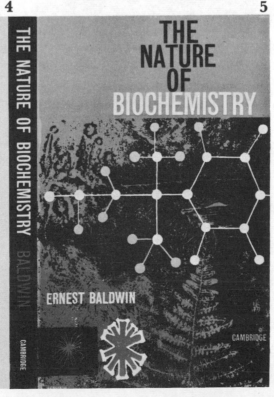

The design shown in **7** is entirely made up of things which relate to the subject, the chemistry of living matter. The front consists of a chemical diagram of living matter, and, at the foot, simple living things. On the back there is a representation of the human organism taken from an old medical book, a diagram of living tissue composed of cells, and another chemical diagram.

1

Posters are also a means of communication, and they often have a pictorial element to make the message more powerful. It is possible that people would not take much notice if the message of a poster were printed in plain type on a white background. It is more likely to do its job well in its pictorial form. But the images used in this way must be carefully chosen, or they will not add much and may even detract from the message. Compare the two posters, **1** and **2**. The first depends upon a play on words. The picture explains the pun but adds nothing to it. It may even make the communication of the message less efficient. The other poster makes its point by graphic means. **1** could just as well, if not better, be expressed by words alone, but **2** stands or falls by its picture. It could not possibly be conveyed in words without loss of meaning and power. It is an excellent example of a message being put over by visual means – true visual communication.

Posters **2** to **7** all make their point by mainly visual means, and in some of them the written message is almost unnecessary. Each of them has a different character because they employ a variety of visual means, each excellently suited to its particular purpose.

2   **3**

FREEDOM FROM HUNGER

smoking is an expensive way of damaging your health

CIGARETTES CAUSE LUNG CANCER

4   **5**

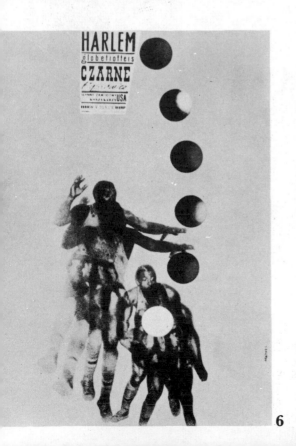

HARLEM
globetrotters
CZARNE
USA

6

honegger
judyta

opera
warszawska

7

6, 7. *Two Polish posters.* **6** *is for the Harlem Globetrotters, an American basketball team, and* **7** *for Honegger's opera 'Judith'.*

1

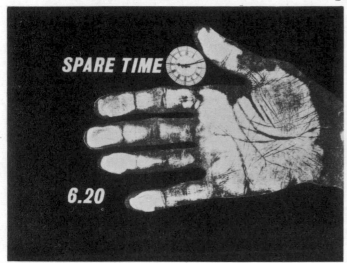

SPARE TIME

6.20

2

FATHER
TAKES
A WIFE

9.15

BBC tv

3

LARAMIE 6.0

BBC tv

4

BBC tv

THE DUKE'S JOURNEY   10.45

5

great flexibility

Each one of the independent wheels is connected to the body by an arm acting as a lever driving a piston which, in turn, in a cylinder acts on an hydraulic fluid which, according to the movement of the piston, compresses more or less a constant volume of gas contained in the suspension sphere which is secured to the body. An entirely leakproof rubber film keeps the gas separated from the hydraulic fluid. Every vertical movement of the wheel acts on the piston which forces the fluid into the cylinder and the lower part of the sphere where it reduces the volume of gas by compressing it in proportions that are greater or smaller according to the initial movement of the wheel. The gas then reacts in accordance with all the proper characteristics of pneumatic springing, in other words, extremely smoothly.

constant height

Every variation of the clearance of the body in comparison with the ground (load variation) operates an automatic clearance correcting device which with the addition or the withdrawal of fluid between the piston and the gas readjusts the vehicle to normal ground clearance (6 1/4 inches).

variable ground clearance

With the help of a simple lever, the driver can, according to his requirements, increase the car's ground clearance when crossing a dip or a ford for example.

aerodynamic design : A simple and logical design gives the DS its clean lines and balanced proportions. Its shape truly fills its purpose : carrying several passengers comfortably, rapidly, safely. Designed with the passengers in mind, the body provides five roomy seats and perfect visibility. The motorist who drives a DS gets the widest possible angle of vision envied by all other motorists in the world. The arrow head profiled front, the smooth lines of the body, a completely smooth underneath are Citroën's answers to wind resistance. Internal streamlining was given the same attention : no radiator grill, carefully designed air channels and circulation under the bonnet.

8

Television titles and trailers, 1, 2, 3, 4, should, like book covers, indicate subject matter and character in a direct visual way. What impression do you get from these designs?
Printed publicity, like other means of visual communication, should be judged by its efficiency. The Austrian package for coffee, 5, tells us unmistakably what is inside. It also manages by the simplest imaginable means to be decorative and suitable to the product. The two pages from a Citroën booklet, 6, 7, make their point by verbal and graphic means harmoniously combined. In 6 the diagrams make the words more vivid and meaningful. In 7 the words stress the importance of the picture. The front of the GPO booklet, 8, conjures up an atmosphere in a way seldom achieved with such economy of effort.

Newspapers are yet another means of communication. Very few people have either the time or the interest to read every single item in a newspaper and the designer must attempt to provide a balanced picture which will give each item on a page the importance it deserves. At the same time the page must be designed in such a way that it can be looked at as a whole and the required item selected. This is a much more difficult problem than it seems to be at first glance, as these examples show. Both muddle and repetitiveness must be avoided, if the newspaper is to be really efficient. The familiar 'unity in diversity' must be the motto.

Visual communications cover a very wide field. They include such things as television trailers and titles, labels, packages, and all kinds of sales literature. We must learn to judge them as we judge other man-made things: by their efficiency. How far do they succeed in transmitting their messages? But this is only the first stage; eventually we shall have to consider the message itself.

3 is the harmonious pattern which we have seen before. To which of the two newspapers, 1 or 2, could it be compared?

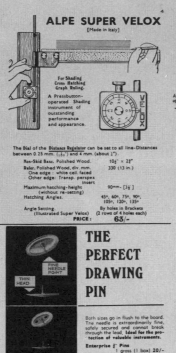

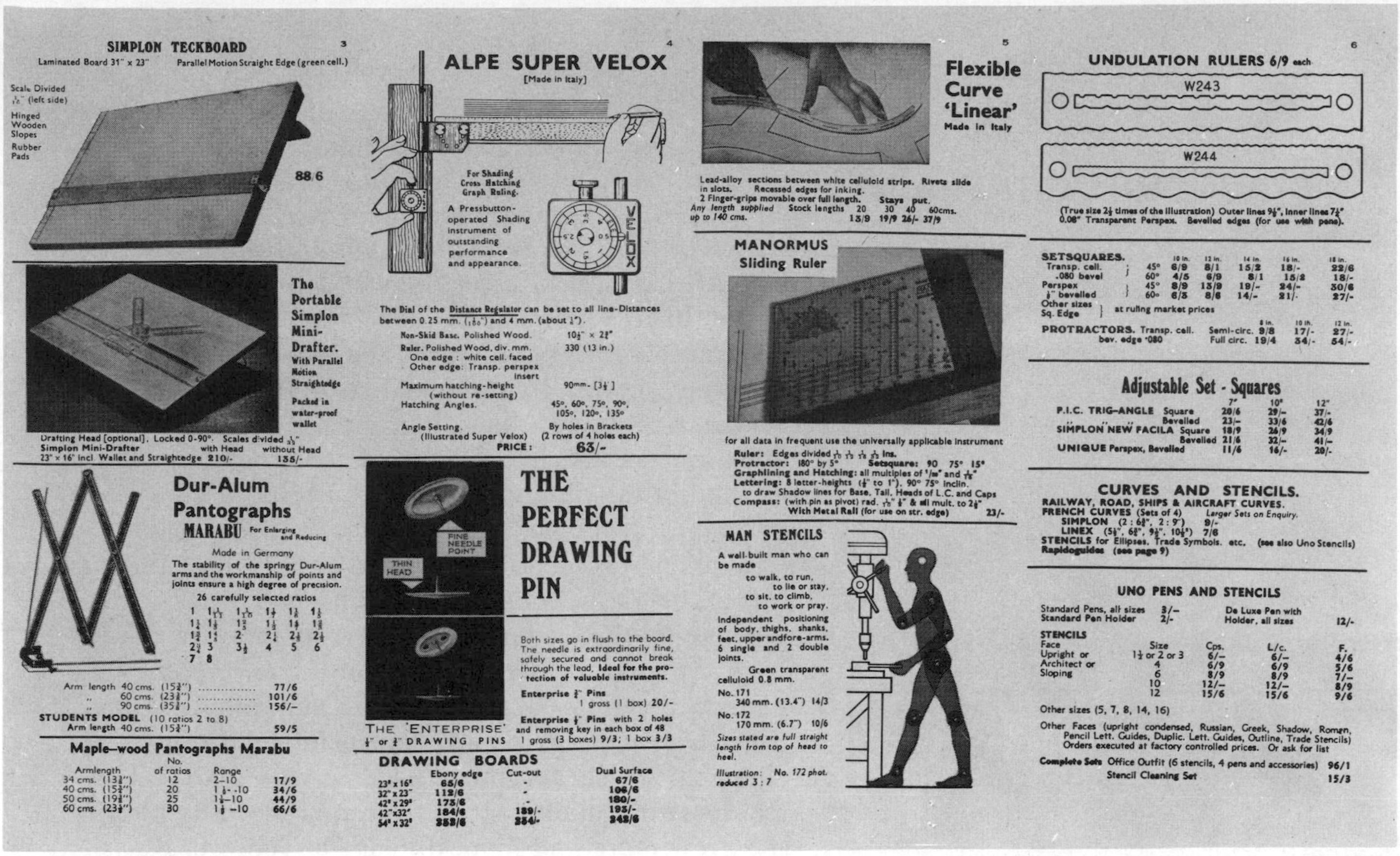

SIMPLON TECKBOARD 3

Laminated Board 31" x 23"   Parallel Motion Straight Edge (green cell.)

Scale Divided 1/10 (left side)
Hinged Wooden Slopes
Rubber Pads

88.6

The Portable Simplon Mini-Drafter

With Parallel Motion Straightedge
Packed in water-proof wallet

Drafting Head (optional). Locked 0-90°. Scales divided 1/10
Simplon Mini-Drafter   with Head   without Head
23" x 16" incl. Wallet and Straightedge 210/-   158/-

Dur-Alum Pantographs

MARABU For Enlarging and Reducing

Made in Germany

The stability of the springy Dur-Alum arms and the workmanship of points and joints ensure a high degree of precision.

26 carefully selected ratios

1	1¼	1⅓	1⅜	1½	1⅝
1¾	1⅞	2	2¼	2½	2¾
2⅓	3⅓	3½	4	5	6
7	8				

Arm length 40 cms. (15¾")	77/6
,, 60 cms. (23¾")	101/6
,, 90 cms. (35¼")	156/-

STUDENTS MODEL (10 ratios 2 to 8)
Arm length 40 cms. (15¾")   59/5

Maple-wood Pantographs Marabu

Armlength	No. of ratios	Range	
34 cms. (13¾")	12	2–10	17/9
40 cms. (15¾")	20	1½–10	34/6
50 cms. (19¾")	25	1½–10	44/9
60 cms. (23¾")	30	1½–10	66/6

ALPE SUPER VELOX 4

[Made in Italy]

For Shading Cross Hatching Graph Ruling.

A Pressbutton-operated Shading instrument of outstanding performance and appearance.

The Dial of the Distance Regulator can be set to all line-Distances between 0.25 mm. (1/100") and 4 mm. (about 1")

Non-Skid Base, Polished Wood.   10½" x 28"
Ruler, Polished Wood, div. mm.   330 (13 in.)
One edge: white cell. faced
Other edge: Transp. perspex insert
Maximum hatching-height (without re-setting)   90mm. [3½]
Hatching Angles.   45°, 60°, 75°, 90°, 105°, 120°, 135°
Angle Setting.   By holes in Brackets
(Illustrated Super Velox)   (2 rows of 4 holes each)
PRICE: 63/-

THE PERFECT DRAWING PIN

FINE NEEDLE POINT
THIN HEAD

Both sizes go in flush to the board. The needle is extraordinarily fine, safely secured and cannot break through the lead. Ideal for the protection of valuable instruments.

Enterprise ½" Pins
  1 gross (1 box) 20/-

Enterprise ¼" Pins with 2 holes and removing key in each box of 48
  1 gross (3 boxes) 9/3; 1 box 3/3

THE 'ENTERPRISE' ¼" or ½" DRAWING PINS

DRAWING BOARDS

	Ebony edge	Cut-out	Dual Surface
23" x 16"	65/6		67/6
32" x 23"	112/6		106/6
42" x 29"	175/6		180/-
42" x 32"	184/6	189/-	195/-
54" x 32"	252/6	254/-	248/6

Flexible Curve 'Linear' 5

Made in Italy

Lead-alloy sections between white celluloid strips. Rivets slide in slots.   Recessed edges for inking.
2 Finger-grips movable over full length.   Stays put.
Any length supplied   Stock lengths 20   30   40   60cms.
up to 140 cms.   13/9   19/9 26/- 37/9

MANORMUS Sliding Ruler

for all data in frequent use the universally applicable instrument

Ruler: Edges divided 1/10 1/50 1/100 ins.
Protractor: 180° by 5°   Setsquare: 90   75°   15°
Graphlining and Hatching: all multiples of 1/16" and 1/10"
Lettering: 8 letter-heights (⅛" to 1"). 90° 75° inclin.
  to draw Shadow lines for Base, Tail, Heads of L.C. and Caps
Compass: (with pin as pivot) rad. 1/10" ¼" & all mult. to 2½"
  With Metal Rail (for use on str. edge)   23/-

MAN STENCILS

A well-built man who can be made
  to walk, to run,
    to lie or stay,
  to sit, to climb,
    to work or pray.
Independent positioning of body, thighs, shanks, feet, upper andfore-arms. 6 single and 2 double joints.

Green transparent celluloid 0.8 mm.
No. 171   340 mm. (13.4") 14/3
No. 172   170 mm. (6.7") 10/6
Sizes stated are full straight length from top of head to heel.

Illustration: No. 172 phot. reduced 3 : 7

UNDULATION RULERS 6/9 each 6

W243
W244

(True size 2½ times of the illustration) Outer lines 9½", Inner lines 7½"
0.08" Transparent Perspex. Bevelled edges (for use with pens).

SETSQUARES.

		10 in.	12 in.	14 in.	16 in.	18 in.
Transp. cell.	45°	6/9	8/1	15/2	18/-	22/6
.080 bevel	60°	4/5	6/9	15/2	18/-	18/-
Perspex	45°	8/9	13/9	19/-	24/-	30/6
¼" bevelled	60°	6/3	8/8	14/-	21/-	22/6
Other sizes Sq. Edge		at ruling market prices				

PROTRACTORS.		8 in.	10 in.	12 in.
Transp. cell.	Semi-circ.	9/8	17/-	27/-
bev. edge .080	Full circ.	19/4	34/-	54/-

Adjustable Set - Squares

		7"	10"	12"
P.I.C. TRIG-ANGLE	Square	20/6	29/-	37/-
,, ,,	Bevelled	23/-	33/-	42/6
SIMPLON NEW FACILA	Square	18/9	24/9	34/9
,, ,,	Bevelled	21/6	32/-	41/-
UNIQUE Perspex, Bevelled		11/6	16/-	20/-

CURVES AND STENCILS.

RAILWAY, ROAD, SHIPS & AIRCRAFT CURVES.
FRENCH CURVES (Sets of 4)   Larger Sets on Enquiry.
SIMPLON (2 : 6⅝", 2 : 9")   9/-
LINEX (5½", 6⅝", 9½", 10½")   7/6
STENCILS for Ellipses, Trade Symbols, etc.   (see also Uno Stencils)
Rapidoguides (see page 9)

UNO PENS AND STENCILS

Standard Pens, all sizes	3/-	De Luxe Pen with	
Standard Pen Holder	2/-	Holder, all sizes	12/-

STENCILS

	Size	Cps.	L/c.	F.
Face	1½ or 2 or 3	6/-	6/-	4/6
Upright or	4	6/9	6/9	4/6
Architect or	6	8/9	8/9	7/-
Sloping	10	12/-	12/-	8/9
	12	15/6	15/6	9/6

Other sizes (5, 7, 8, 14, 16)

Other Faces (upright condensed, Russian, Greek, Shadow, Roman, Pencil Lett. Guides, Duplic. Lett. Guides, Outline, Trade Stencils) Orders executed at factory controlled prices. Or ask for list

Complete Sets Office Outfit (6 stencils, 4 pens and accessories) 96/1
  Stencil Cleaning Set   15/3

EXERCISES

1. Examine the catalogue, **4**, and decide whether it is an efficient design.

2. Which of the two letterheads, **5**, **6**, do you prefer and why?

3. Compare **3**, page 64, with **5**, page 65. Explain in detail which you prefer.

4. Look at illustrated books, including instruction books, brochures, posters and other printed matter and discuss them from the point of view of (a) efficiency and (b) visual harmony.

5. Look at all the different signs in the nearest shopping street in your town or district. Explain whether, in your opinion, anything could be done to improve (a) the signs and (b) the relationships between them.

5   **6**

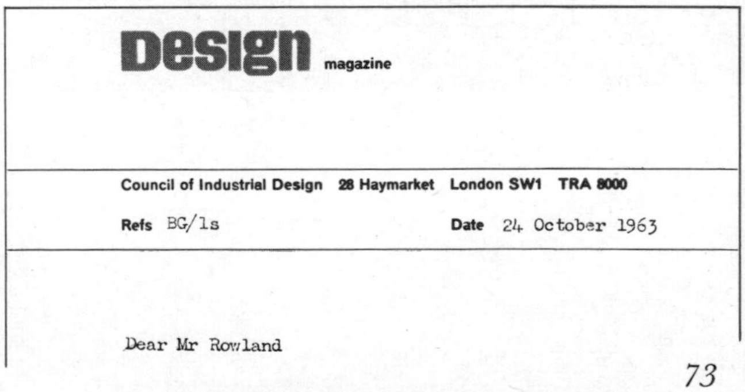

CONTRACTORS TO THE ADMIRALTY, WAR OFFICE, MINISTRY OF AVIATION, AIR MINISTRY, U.K. A.E.A AND POSTMASTER GENERAL ON GOVERNMENT CONTROLLED LIST

LONDON OFFICE 109 KINGSWAY W.C.2   M.O.A. APPROVED   REF. NO. 41147   LONDON TELEGRAMS:
TELEPHONE : HOLBORN 3074   A.R.B. APPROVED   NO. AI/6560/62   WHITLECT WESTCENT, LONDON
  DESIGNERS AND   MANUFACTURERS   OVERSEAS CABLES
  OF ELECTRONIC   EQUIPMENT   WHITLECT, LONDON, W.C.2

WHITELEY ELECTRICAL RADIO CO. LTD.

DIRECTORS: A.H. WHITELEY, M.B.E. (MANAGING) · B.C WHITELEY · R.T. LAKIN, M.B.E., M.I.E.E., M.Brit., I.R.E.

TELEPHONES	REGISTERED OFFICE	TELEGRAMS
MANSFIELD 1762·3·4·5	RADIO WORKS VICTORIA ST	WHITEBON, MANSFIELD

REGD TRADE MARK

YOUR REF   CMP   **MANSFIELD** NOTTS   OUR REF RTL/EE. DATE 14th January, 1964.

ALL COMMUNICATIONS MUST BE ADDRESSED TO THE COMPANY AT THE ABOVE REGISTERED OFFICE

Design magazine

Council of Industrial Design   28 Haymarket   London SW1   TRA 8000

Refs BG/ls   Date 24 October 1963

Dear Mr Rowland

4

What is a visual language?

In Part Two we discussed how man-made shapes and patterns come about: why new materials, new processes of manufacture and new functions have far-reaching effects on the appearance of the things we make; how the state of society and the mental climate of a period affect the works produced by men of the time. A study of the development of the chair, for example, shows not only how chair-makers gradually learnt more about their craft and the materials they were handling, but also how people's ideas and habits changed. In the same way the Gothic method of building was evolved in response to a number of technological problems, but social and economical problems also had to be solved at the same time. The early Romanesque cathedrals were made possible by the availability of cheap labour which could be used for the transport of the enormous masses of stone necessary for these buildings. But as times became more secure and social conditions changed this cheap labour became very scarce. The transport of building stone from quarry to building site grew more and more difficult to achieve. Raw materials became scarcer and more costly. Architects had to find a method of building larger churches to accommodate the growing congregations, with higher towers to express the growing importance of towns, but at the same time they needed to use less building stone than in the smaller, lower Romanesque churches. We know how ingeniously they accomplished this seemingly impossible task. But they did more than that: they also expressed the mood of their times. The tall tapering spires and towers with their fine tracery, the lofty arches and vaults, the buttresses with their pinnacles, all these pointed to heaven and so expressed the deep religious feeling of the period. And we can go even further in trying to understand why Gothic churches and cathedrals were built as they were.

1 *The triumphs of medieval architecture were made possible by many technological advances, not least those which saved human labour. The wheelbarrow, 1, with its neck strap, allowed one worker to do the kind of job which formerly was done by two.*

Medieval man tried to solve his problems and doubts by seeking enlightenment in the Scriptures and by speculation. Scientific facts were accepted only if they were based on pure speculation. Anything derived from observation of nature was mistrusted. This seems strange to us, for we live in an age when all scientific knowledge is based on observation. The experiments you conduct in chemistry and biology classes teach you many facts, and, even more important, they teach you the basic principle that there can be no knowledge without observation. If, however, a medieval scholar wanted to find out something he would sit down and speculate and would not allow anything he might have observed in the living world around him to influence his thought in any way. A story tells how two scholars of that period sat arguing with a student. In the course of their argument the question arose as to the number of teeth in a horse's mouth. As neither scholar knew the number, they fetched several heavy tomes, where they expected to find the necessary information. After many hours' search they had still not found it. At this stage the student suggested that perhaps it would be simpler to go to the stable and count the actual teeth in the mouth of a living horse. This idea so revolted and disgusted the scholars that they threw the student out and then returned to their ancient text. They must have felt rather as a modern scientist might feel if one of his students were to suggest he should read the tea leaves in order to solve a scientific problem.

Instead of using practical experiments to test their theories and to support them, medieval scholars presented their ideas in a very special way. A medieval learned book, for instance, would be divided into parts, further subdivided into questions, the questions into articles, and the articles into still smaller parts, the whole forming a network of interdependent ideas, none of which could stand alone. Where a modern book may consist of chapters, with perhaps some subdivisions, a medieval work would contain thousands of little sections and sub-sections, all working together like a machine in which nothing is independent of the rest. This complicated structure of thought was firmly held together by the main argument. The overall pattern

2

3

The eleventh-century illustration of the building of a church, 2, and the twelfth-century carving showing the Adoration of the Magi, 3, look strange to us today, but they undoubtedly looked correct to their contemporaries. What connection can you find between these pictures and the story of the two scholars on this page?

of such a work, in spite of its many subdivisions, could always be perceived.

There is a striking similarity between this weblike structure of medieval thought and the structure of a medieval church, **1**. The ground plan of a Gothic church or cathedral almost looks as though someone had attempted to draw the diagram of a learned work of the same period. The structure of a Gothic cathedral reveals the technological advances which made such a building possible. It can also show the attitude of mind which made the building necessary. This principle, as we shall see, applies to all periods.

There is an amusing story of an Italian painter who made a portrait of an Eastern ruler. When the ruler saw the picture he was aghast. He had sat for his portrait wearing a beautiful, clean, bright red fez, but in the picture the fez was dirty on one side. Patiently the painter explained how the colour of an object changes when it is turned away from the light, but the ruler would have none of it. He took the fez from his head and turned it over in his hands again and again. 'Look', he said, 'it is red all the way round.'

Now you may think that this ruler was extremely silly and did not use his eyes properly. And yet he was not nearly as silly as he may seem, for we all behave rather as he did, in one way or another. We never just *see* the things around us; we always see what we *want* to see or what we *know*. In this drawing, **2**, most people will see a vase. Once, however, you are told that it also represents the profiles of two people facing each other, you will be able to interpret it in this way too, and will even be able to switch your interpretation from one to the other. In other words, you will see what you want to see, or what you know to be there, at will. This is really a crude example, but the following one is rather less obvious. Illustrations **3** to **5** show three profiles. One is of a young woman, another of an old one, while the third is ambiguous; it can be seen as the profile of either a young or an old woman. A number of experiments have shown that the way in which we see (and interpret) this last picture will largely depend on how we are prepared for it. Those people who are shown the drawing of the young woman first will almost inevitably see the ambiguous

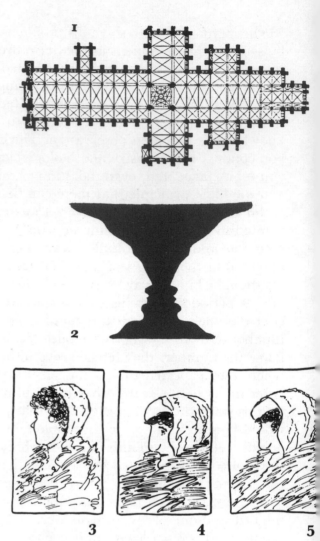

The nineteenth-century drawing of Chartres Cathedral, **6**, varies considerably from the modern photograph, **7**. Why did the artist, who set out to give a true account of the building, not succeed in doing so? During the nineteenth century people held very strong opinions about the Gothic style – it was considered the holiest style to which man could aspire. When the artist drew this great building he, perhaps quite unconsciously, reflected the ideas of his society and times. He changed the proportions to make it look even more lofty and spiritual than the original architects had intended. The earlier round arches have become pointed. This drawing is the outcome not only of the artist's observation but also the ideas which surrounded him.

6

7

picture as a young woman, while those who are shown the picture of the old woman first will see it as a picture of an old woman. The world is full of ambiguous objects like the third picture. Whenever we are faced with one – and that is much more often than we realise – and are forced to interpret it, we draw quite unconsciously on what we have already seen: on our visual knowledge and experience. In fact, we never see merely what is in front of us; our vision is always influenced by a number of other things no matter how hard we try to keep them away. When a painter paints a picture it can never be wholly true to nature, for the painter uses his knowledge and experience to interpret the things he sees. What he puts down in paint will be a record of his vision, of his knowledge, and of his experience.

Let us put it another way. Imagine you are going to an art class, and on the way everything possible has gone wrong. You lost some money on the bus, missed your stop while looking for it on the floor, ended by not finding it, had to walk back to where you should have got off, slipped and dirtied your coat because you were hurrying, got to the class late, and as soon as you arrived were informed that your picture had not been selected for the exhibition. By the time you have reached the class, as a result of your various mishaps, you feel rather depressed. You begin to paint a picture and, as you become engrossed by it, you forget your sad experiences. But have you really forgotten? Somehow your picture has a rather melancholy air. Without your being aware of it, your mood has come through and is present in your picture. How can this come about? In various ways. For instance, you may have preferred the sad colours on your palette to the others, so that your picture will tend to have more blues and purples in it than gay reds and yellows. The picture will tend to be sad not because you decided to paint a sad picture – you did not – but because you rejected most of the colours which might have made it a cheerful one. This is why a picture may be sad, even if it does not depict a sad event, or why music may be sad: it is simply because the painter or composer rejected, quite unconsciously, everything that might have made it gay.

We can apply this in a much wider sense. The artist reflects in his work not only his immediate personal feelings and way of thinking, but also his knowledge and experience of the world around him. All that his community thinks, feels, and desires will, in the way we have discussed, influence him, find expression in his work and give it a certain mood or flavour. This is how the spirit of the times is often revealed in the works of man. This spirit is infinitely complicated and subtle, but if we are to get a true picture of any period in history we must try to understand it. It expresses the collective state of mind of the people who lived at the time: their hopes and aspirations, their loves and hates, their fears and frustrations. The things man makes reflect this collective state of mind, this spirit of the times, this mental climate. When we look at the architecture of the Middle Ages and compare it with the sculpture, the painting, the manner of writing, the engineering, the layout of towns and all other visual aspects of the period, we find a relationship between them, a character which they all share. This relationship is an unconscious expression of the times: a visual language which relates and unites the different works of a particular period. It is fitted only to the conditions which brought it about.

The five pictures on these pages sum up in a very simplified form the visual language of the Middle Ages. It was a devout period; to medieval men the spiritual side of life was more important than physical reality. Church architecture was the most dominating feature. The church marked the centre of the town and its activities; but it also expressed the spirit of the town and of its religion. The flying buttresses and pinnacles, 5, are engineering structures but they point to heaven and so help to express the loftiness of religious thought. Ideas and technology support each other. The comparative unimportance of the individual and the overwhelming importance of the community, both religious and civic, is given expression in the twelfth-century statues of saints from Chartres cathedral, 3. They are elongated to fit into the general vertical pattern of the cathedral and to become part of the structure. The pattern of their garments forms an almost geometric arrangement, their postures are uniform, they have little individuality; in fact they are not meant to be seen as real people. Like the structure of the church, they symbolise the soul of Christianity. Similarly, the artist who made the painting of the Annunciation, 4, did not try to describe something he had seen in real life, but an emotion. The figures have little to do with reality, they are not ordinary human beings but have an air of other-worldliness which is accentuated by their isolation in empty space. In the stained glass design, 1, the verticality of the figures is once again pronounced. The emphasis is on their spiritual nature. Even medieval writing, 2, seems to share the same character. In looking at these pictures we must remember that the visual language of the Middle Ages was also related to materials and processes, as these examples amply testify.

1   2

5

By the fourteenth century the medieval spirit was on the wane. With the rise of a new merchant class, the organisation of the medieval town began to crack. As international trade increased, old loyalties to the town began to disappear and the old system could no longer cope with modern conditions. Many industries were now carried on outside the towns, a state of affairs which conflicted with the interests of the guilds. Industry, trade and banking could no longer be contained within the walls of the medieval town. Nations grew up and the importance of towns became less and less. The new merchant class, with its international rather than local connections, created new values: buying and manufacturing, selling, and counting money.

At about that time, people began to discover the great Greek and Roman civilisations of antiquity. Classical authors were read again, and people realised that the medieval order of things was not necessarily the best; that vast civilisations had existed, based on a different order, not centred in the church and its dogmas or in the closely-knit organisation of medieval society. The ideas of antiquity gained acceptance. The most important outcome of this change in outlook was that people began to enquire into the nature of things instead of accepting traditional explanations. An unprecedented period of enquiry followed. The laws of the natural world were investigated: modern science was born. This period has been given the name of Renaissance, or Rebirth, because the ideas of antiquity were born again.

1

To fit the changed conditions of life and the new ideas which exercised men's minds, a new visual language was evolved. Life in Europe did not of course change overnight, and the new visual language of the Renaissance took shape very slowly. If you look at the thirteenth-century stone carving from Chartres, **2**, and compare it with the twelfth-century carving, also from Chartres, page 79, **3**, you will notice the change of attitude.

The geometrical pattern of the folds of the garments on page 79 has given way to a more natural pattern in **2** opposite; the sculptor has obviously looked at real people. Not only are the later figures less elongated but they are treated as individuals, not merely as props for the building. Their postures are different from each other, as are their faces and expressions. Compared to the twelfth-century sculpture they seem to have come to life, stepped forward from the church wall and left their haloes behind. The sculpture from Strasbourg Cathedral, made about 1260, **1**, shows a similar development. Real life seems to have inspired this animated group. The figures are not remote from everyday life, as in the earlier sculpture. They are real people, in various states of agitation, who show their emotions. In the sculpture on page 79 the drapery is largely ornamental, and has little to do with the body which it covers, but in the Strasbourg carving we can almost feel the human limbs beneath. The sculptor must have looked very closely at life around him in order to achieve such natural postures. One artist of this period was known to have opened the window of his studio and painted what he saw outside. What do you think the two medieval scholars who looked for the number of a horse's teeth in a book instead of in the horse's mouth would have thought of such an activity? Actions of this kind did much to undermine the medieval belief that knowledge must never be based on observation but only on speculation. Gradually the medieval way of thinking fell into disrepute; a new spirit was afoot. The medieval vision was dying.

3

*The changed attitude affected everything people made. The Gothic way of building continued for a long time but it was gradually modified to reveal a different attitude of mind. Picture **3** (Henry VII's Chapel, Westminster Abbey), shows that as vaulting became more and more ornate the earlier fusion of belief and technology suffered. This vaulting, in spite of its magnificence, no longer aspires to heaven. The energy of the heavenward urge of the earlier Gothic churches seems to have gone; the ceiling has become more horizontal and flatter, and the pattern of the ribs aimless.*

The emergence of this new spirit can be clearly seen by comparing two paintings made on either side of the 'turn of the thirteenth century: **1**, the Virgin and Child by Cimabue (1240–1302), painted in 1280, and **2**, the painting of the same subject by Cimabue's pupil Giotto (1266–1337), painted in 1310. In spite of the comparatively short space of time which separates these two paintings, and the similarity of subjects, a definite change is evident, an evolution from one kind of painting to another. Cimabue painted this religious scene in the visual language of his time, a language which still belonged to the medieval tradition. The painting is a flat pattern, but here and there, especially in the faces and the architectural structure, we can see traces of a third dimension. It is as though the painter were trying to say something which had never been said before, and for which he could not find the words. The real break with the past, the birth of a new visual language, came with Giotto. Where in Cimabue's painting the drapery is largely decorative, in Giotto's the folds disappear here and there, the cloth tightens, to show the solidity of the body inside. Some people might say that the great refinement and delicacy of Cimabue's way of painting have been lost – compare the child's elegant posture and the movement of his right hand to those in Giotto's painting. Cimabue's two columns of angels' heads lead the eye from either side to the Virgin's face; the lowest head in each column is tilted in the opposite direction, adding rhythm to the whole composition. Giotto's work has none of these things.

It could be said that the faces and bodies in his painting are clumsy and graceless by the side of Cimabue's subtly drawn faces and figures. But if they are clumsy it is the clumsiness of the real world of flesh and blood. Giotto's painting is not composed as a flat pattern, but in depth. Notice how the effect of light and shade on the two screens is observed, how the recess in which the holy group is placed is hollowed out. Cornices and ledges recede into space; light plays on solid objects. One can feel the weight of the bodies and experience the space in which they exist. The painting bears the true marks of the Renaissance which was to come. Artists, like other people, are influenced by the world around them. The teachings of St. Francis, who wanted people to think of all living things as their brothers, the dissatisfaction with medieval ideas and the medieval mode of life already in the air, caused Giotto to look more closely at the world, at a time when most other artists were continuing to paint – although often with real skill and great feeling – what they had been taught to see. Giotto's people are real people with solid bodies and human emotions. We identify ourselves with them, so that their grief becomes our grief and their joy our joy. We must not, however, suppose that Giotto woke up one morning and said, 'From today I am going to paint things in the round.' He learned slowly to express the mood of his time and quite unconsciously evolved a new visual language to describe it. The visual language used by Cimabue could no longer express the things which he saw, knew and felt.

This way of looking at the world was quite new. It must have seemed strange to most people and some must have muttered something about 'modern art'. But soon other artists discovered the new way of looking and painting. Whereas in the past painters had tried to produce pictures which looked still and unreal, they now attempted and often achieved the opposite: pictures full of the life they saw around them. How was this achieved? There was only one way: by observing and exploring nature and discovering its laws. This is why the artists of the Renaissance were so often at the same time scientists and mathematicians.

Leonardo, about the end of the fifteenth century, defending the new scientific spirit of enquiry, said, '. . . it seems to me that those sciences are vain and full of error which do not spring from experiment, the source of all certainty . . .'

This was the atmosphere in which the men of the Renaissance worked out their own visual language as the men of the middle ages had done before them. In order to describe the world around them more fully the artists of the Renaissance had to find a means of showing relationships between objects in space. In this they had an aim in common with the architects of the period.

Towns were beginning to be laid out and planned as a series of vistas of churches, palaces and houses. The architects who planned these towns had to find a means of developing their ideas and so were faced by much the same problems as the painters. The science of perspective which provided the solution of these problems was invented by an architect, Brunelleschi. The artists of the Renaissance used perspective as a tool for investigating the natural world. Leonardo and other painters examined the anatomy of the human body and of other living things, in order to understand and express the truth which they sought in nature. They were ready to make discoveries and tried always to look with fresh eyes. When Leonardo saw that sunlight cast blue shadows onto a white surface, he made a great observation, well in advance of his time, which was not taken up by scientists and artists until the nineteenth century.

1

2

To the medieval artist relationships between objects in space – spatial relationships – were not very important. In the painting of the murder of St. Thomas Becket, 1, made about 1200, the spatial relationship between the figures is almost ignored, as is the relationship between figures and building. Compare this with the Renaissance drawing, 2, in which the figures and the space which surrounds them can be experienced, even though everything is only roughly sketched in. We get quite a

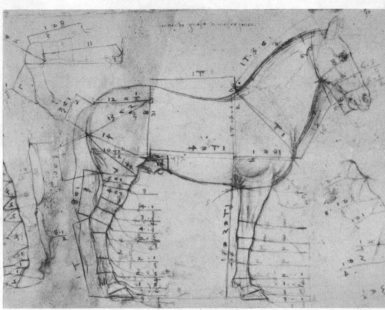

5 **6**

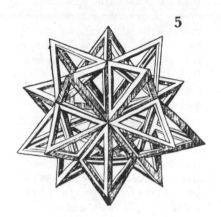

*good idea of the place depicted in
this drawing, while we cannot even
guess what the place shown in* **1**
looked like.

*Research into the physical world
went on in many directions. The
laws of foreshortening were
investigated by methods such as the
one shown by Dürer in 1525,* **3**.
*The drawing of the horse with
dimensions marked,* **4**, *and the
drawing of the complex
geometrical form,* **5**, *indicate other
pursuits of Renaissance artists.
Man also was subjected to
investigation: his anatomy, his
character, his emotions, his nobility,
and,* **6**, *his absurdity.*

The architecture which emerged from the new ideas of the Renaissance was vastly different from the architecture of the Middle Ages, which seemed unsatisfactory in the new mental climate. The church of St. Andrea, Mantua, designed by Alberti in 1470, **1, 2**, is typical of this new architecture. Renaissance architects made use of the methods of the Greeks and Romans, applying these methods to the needs of their own time. We can see that the Gothic method of vaulting has been given up, columns abandoned and replaced by pilasters – flattened columns incorporated in the wall. Instead of the forest of columns of a Gothic church, supporting many vaults, we experience here one vast space, modelled, as it were, by the architect. The plan of this church shows that the aisles familiar in earlier churches have been transformed into a series of side chapels which are closely linked to the nave and to the central space. Medieval man had looked towards heaven: in a Gothic church our gaze is directed upwards away from the earth. Renaissance man remained with his feet firmly on the ground, and this accounts for the changed emphasis of Renaissance architecture. Cornices, ledges and mouldings all combine to create a horizontal effect. The upward-surging steeple is replaced by a dome. The great harmony and unity of St. Andrea, Mantua, rests on the use of a set of proportions which have been applied to every part of it. Alberti has also created a harmonious relationship between the interior and the exterior by the use of the same paired giant pilasters, identical in detail, arrangement and proportion, so that the rhythm and proportion of the inside is continued on the façade. This church expresses the new Christianity of the Renaissance and had a lasting influence on generations of later architects.

ras igitur animantes hominis tantummo-
do causa factas esse appareret. mundum
utique hominis dum taxat gratia á deo factum & constitutum fuisse concluderetur.
quoniam ipsum propter animantes factum
& eas propter hominem factas dicamu es:
At hoc ipsum ex eo certum esse declaratur:
quod omnia quecunque facta sunt soli ho-
mini deseruire ac mirum in modum famu-
lari meridiana ut dicitur luce clarius con-
spicimus: quo quidem probato uereq conces-
so, hominem cuius gratia mundum creatú
confitemur: utique á deo factum fuisse ma-
nifestum est. Unde friuole & uane de for-
matione hominis cunctorum poetarum opi-

Similar ideas helped to produce the calligraphy of the period. Like the architects, the scribes went back for their letter forms to earlier models which accorded with their thoughts and feelings. This writing of about 1450, **3**, has a round, open character, like the architecture of the time, and contrasts with the angular verticality of Gothic writing (*page 78*, **2**).

Painting also developed from Giotto's day onwards in the spirit of the Renaissance. For the first time in the modern era landscape becomes a part of pictures. Even though this painting of the Resurrection, by Piero della Francesca, **4**, has a spiritual subject, observation of everyday life is evident. The way in which objects recede into the picture, as does the second head from the left, has been thoroughly examined. The scientific spirit can also be seen in the composition of the picture: certain spiritual ideas have been interpreted in a geometric form. For instance, the strange arrangement of the trees is not accidental but has a definite purpose in the scheme of this painting. If each row of trees were continued into the foreground they would meet along the line formed by the staff in Christ's right hand: the staff would be common to both rows. Lines roughly connecting the bottom ends of the trees would converge at the bottom end of the staff. We can also see that the trees on the left are old and dead whilst those on the right are young and in leaf. Christ's staff bearing the sign of the cross becomes therefore a symbolic link between life and death. Similarly, lines roughly connecting the heads of the sleeping soldiers would meet in Christ's left hand, making it a symbol of mankind's true rallying point. In this great painting many other ideas are expressed in visual terms. For instance, the feeling of rising up – the idea of the Resurrection – is stressed by the upward-surging triangle formed by Christ's upper arms and head, which forms a strong contrast with the heavy, horizontal tomb. The pictures on these two pages give us a glimpse of the visual language of the Renaissance which we understand fully only if we relate it to the mental climate of the period.

The change in the way people thought and planned had an effect on the way they looked at the world around them. In order to express this new outlook they invented a new visual language. While Giotto may still have had some things in common with Cimabue, men of the later Renaissance had little to link them with their medieval predecessors, and the visual languages of the two periods were not only different but also unintelligible to each other. When people of the fifteenth century looked at the cathedrals of the twelfth century they found them unrefined and tasteless. These men were completely out of sympathy with the earlier visual language. Medieval times were considered uncultured, what we should now call barbaric. In those days the word 'barbaric' did not have this meaning and the word to use was 'Gothic', so they called that period the 'Gothic period' as a term of abuse.

EXERCISES

1. What is a visual language?
2. What is a mental climate?
3. Do you think a visual language is important to society and to each individual person? Why?
4. What are the main differences between the visual language of the Middle Ages and that of the Renaissance? In your answer refer to the reasons for the differences and use sketches and diagrams where applicable.
5. What is a spatial relationship?
6. List the visual devices used by Mantegna in 'The Agony in the Garden', **1**, which make it a true Renaissance painting. Explain why it could not have been painted during the Middle Ages.
7. Explain why Alberti's St. Andrea could not have been built during the Middle Ages.

*Mantegna's 'Agony in the Garden', **1**, is a typical Renaissance painting, and incorporates many of the visual devices of the period. The landscape is painted in depth, an effect which is largely achieved by the skilful use of colour. Perspective plays an important part in this painting. By its use the artist lets us see the fortified town from a low eye level, which makes it look particularly forbidding. In the face and figure of Jesus perspective is used to give a completely different effect. Here the low eye level lends an air of nobility and differentiates Christ from the three sleeping apostles, who almost seem part of the layered rock. Because we see Christ's face from below we gain insight into his spiritual solitude. The much foreshortened figure of the apostle on the right leads the eye into the picture, along the water's edge, past the figure of Judas and, following the zig-zagging line of soldiers, into the town. We are therefore invited to explore the depth of the painting. This movement of the eye is countered by the forward movement of the soldiers, which is also emphasised by the rhythm of the rock formation. At the same time the drama of the situation has not prevented the artist from showing his interest in rabbits, waterbirds and plants. Paintings like these were important not only in their own right, but also on account of the influence they had on lesser artists. During the Middle Ages most religious themes were copied again and again in the same way – nature was rarely observed. Picture **2** shows a painting from an illuminated manuscript depicting Christ in the Temple. You can see that the hands and faces of the Elders, who are expressing surprise, were all done to a pattern and not derived from a study of people. The background is empty and there is no feeling of space. When the lessons of Renaissance painting had been absorbed by lesser painters and illustrators, their works too began to change. **3** shows a miniature painting in a book. The Flemish painter who made it was not such a great master as Mantegna, but he was influenced by the great painters, who made him realise how to explore the world around him with his eyes. This was one of the ways in which the visual language and the ideas of the Renaissance spread all over Europe.*

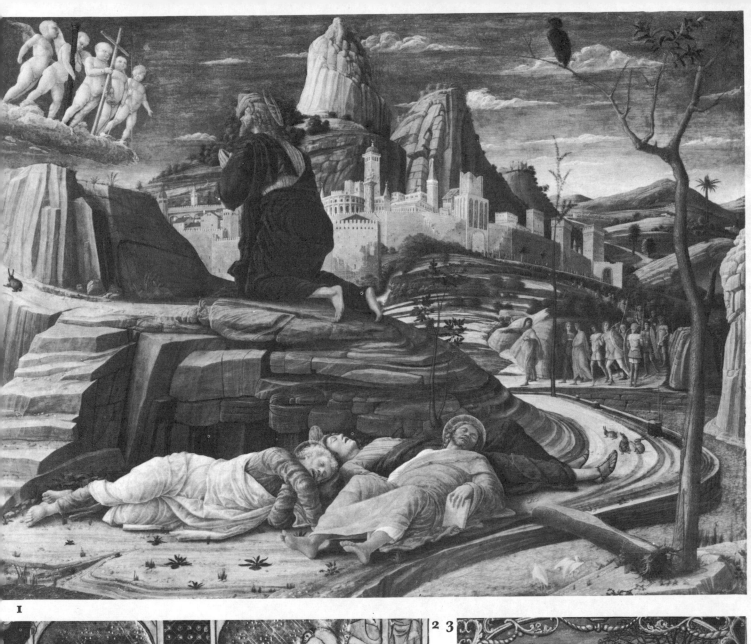

1

2 3

2

8. Look at the Gothic church in picture **1** and guess in which century it was built. Notice especially the strong horizontal lines, the ornate buttresses, the dome-like pinnacles.

9. Look at the architect's drawing, **2**, and guess in which century it was *drawn*.

10. Picture **3** shows a number of random sketches of convicts drawn from memory by a doctor who considered them a good likeness. Picture **4** shows a series of random tracings taken from photographs of convicts from police files. Picture **3** suggests that most convicts have definite criminal characteristics, but this does not seem to be confirmed by the tracings from photographs. The draughtsman was obviously influenced by the knowledge that he was sketching convicts, while the camera suffered from no such influence. Compare this with pictures **6** and **7** on pages 76 and 77. Describe other examples to demonstrate the influence of ideas on what we think we see. Use sketches where appropriate.

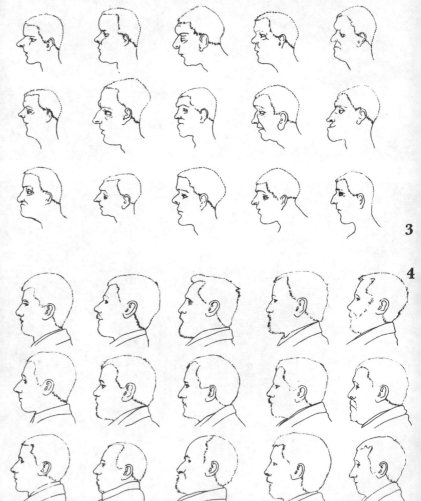

3

4

5

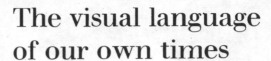

The visual language of our own times

Modern times may be said to have started in the nineteenth century. Physicists, biologists, and other scientists made many startling discoveries which shook our old world in its foundations and opened up new horizons which must have seemed fantastic at the time. Many of our old notions which we had believed for centuries and on which our lives were modelled were now found to be untrue and had to be abandoned. With them went many of our most cherished beliefs, while others were severely shaken. Doctors, psychiatrists, and others discovered hidden depths in the human mind which forced us to re-examine our ideas about human nature and made us look at ourselves and our fellow humans in an altogether different light. These and many other discoveries showed that the superficial aspect of things is often misleading. That which we used to refer to as 'reality' turned out to be not the ultimate truth, but only a half-way stage. The 'real' world came to be looked at as an outer shell of nature which had to be pierced if one was to get at the truth. For it was realised that without an understanding of this deeper reality our experience of the world must remain as incomplete as our experience of a book which we may look at but cannot read. These startling results of man's researches into his surroundings were made possible through a painstaking *analysis*, that is to say, a searching examination, even taking things apart and examining the parts.

This analytical approach was not confined to scientists but used with equal effect by others – amongst them artists. For very similar reasons – to gain a more complete experience and vision of the world around them – artists made use of analytical methods in the second half of the nineteenth century, with equally astonishing results. Scientists did not influence artists in this to any great extent, rather can it be said that both attacked their own problems in a similar fashion. Their findings were often remarkably similar.

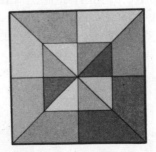

1

*In diagram **1** two balloons are suspended at the end of a dark passage. If one of them is slowly inflated and the other deflated they will both appear to be moving – the inflated one forwards and the deflated one backwards. In picture **2** a number of odd shapes are suspended in a certain arrangement so that when they are viewed end-on a symmetrical pattern appears. These are just two examples of the ways in which our eyes can give us the wrong impression of the world around us. Modern artists often mistrust visual impressions such as were accepted by Renaissance artists.*

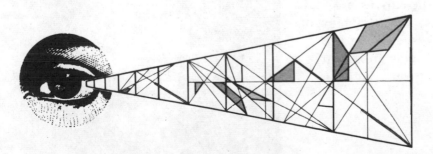

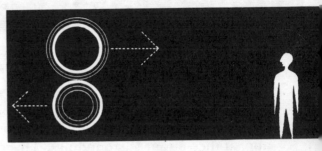

2

1. *This is a charming picture, but it shows no real advance in technique or ideas since the greatest period of Renaissance painting. It expresses the ideas of a small minority who were out of touch with the real problems of their age, so that by its very nature it could not provide a new visual language. This artist was merely repeating what had been done before, like the artist who painted picture **2**, page 89. Impressionists, by contrast, took the kind of visual investigation which was started during the Renaissance one stage further. They created visual analysis. Instead of examining the external*

The world, after this period of feverish activity, could never be the same again. As a result of the work of the early pioneers in science and in art, man's attitude to the world began to change long before the effects of twentieth century technology began to change the appearance of our surroundings. This change was characterised by a new *scepticism*, that is to say a mistrust of the old-established laws, and even of appearances. This led, amongst other things, to a re-examination of the relationship between man and nature, and between man and man.

The first analytical period in art occurred in the third quarter of the nineteenth century. The idea of light was very much in people's minds. There were new optical theories about. New methods of construction made it possible to admit more light into the interior of buildings.

Artists, giving expression to this interest, realised that an analysis of light would help them to record many of the fleeting effects of light and shade. By putting little dabs of pure colour side by side on the canvas, instead of mixing them on the palette, these painters achieved brilliant results. Blue and yellow interspersed in this way will give green, the two colours being mixed in the viewer's eye as it were, and this green is much

*appearance of things they
tried to analyse the nature of
light, which transmits appearance
to us. Instead of copying colours
they re-created them. Many of
the rich patrons who were used
to the highly finished surfaces of
nineteenth-century paintings
objected to the coarse quality of
the paint and the lack of detail
in Impressionist paintings, **3**.
(**2** is an enlarged detail from **3**.)
The total effect of an
Impressionist painting is to give
a visual impression in terms of
the materials used, in this case
oil paint. Such a painting also
expresses the way people
thought and felt at the
beginning of the modern era
of scientific analysis.*

2   3

more vibrant and alive than any colour that could be
mixed on the palette. By using only a few bright
colours, but changing the proportions of the dabs,
all the colours of nature could be reproduced.
Impressionism, as this method of painting was called,
was the first analytical painting of modern times. The
Impressionists, however, although they analysed and
recreated the superficial aspect of forms, did not go
very far in their analysis of the forms themselves.

1

These paintings are really
analyses. The forms are
analysed into their
constituent planes as a
geometrical form might be
analysed. This was not
an entirely new principle, it
had been thought of before,
as drawing **5**, made by
Dürer in 1516, proves.
But Cézanne took it a stage
further, applying it to whole
pictures. Through his
analysis he showed us his
world. Scientists of his time
were also using analytical
methods to explore the
natural world.

2

The analysis of form had been attempted by various artists, but it was left to Paul Cézanne to bring to it the modern scientific spirit.

The Impressionists had shown us a world which depended more on the nature of the light than on the character of the objects. Cézanne rebelled against this attitude and attempted to come to grips with the objects themselves. Where the Impressionists had often given us different views in different lighting conditions of the same object, or scene, Cézanne looked for the character of what he saw. Furthermore he was convinced that most people, deceived by their senses, obtain a faulty and muddled vision of the world. To him the purpose of the artist must be to bring order to our experience of the world, to sort out our impressions, to analyse them and fit them into a conception of nature which would be 'true'. This was not so far removed from the aims of the scientists of his period, but being an artist he set about it in a different way. He felt and knew that behind the superficial aspect of nature there was an underlying structure to be discovered. In the course of a lifetime, with the determination and tenacity of a scientist, he analysed the world around him in order to discover its basic shapes, its structures, its character, its truth. From letters which he wrote to friends we know that he looked for geometric forms in nature: the cone, the cube, the cylinder and the sphere.

Cézanne was a great painter, and he occupies a place in the development of painting comparable to that held by Giotto six centuries earlier. As in Giotto's day, the visual language of the period was no longer adequate to express the new thoughts and feelings. Both Giotto and Cézanne prepared the way for later developments.

3 is a late landscape painting by Cézanne. Compare it with earlier landscapes, 1, 2.
4 is a self-portrait by Cézanne.

4

5

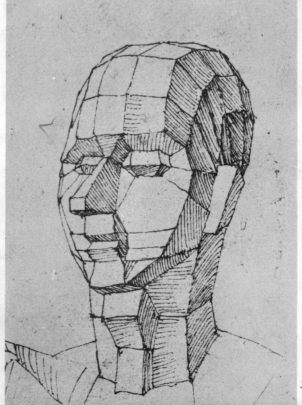

3

1

4

2

5

3

6

7

10

8

9

A scientist wishing to discover the essential nature of a substance often analyses it into its component parts. When he has discovered its true nature in this way, he may carry out a synthesis (putting together) of the components in order to make a new substance. In doing this he will probably purify and re-arrange them in such a way that the new substance has certain advantages over the original one. Looking at the work of Picasso one is aware of a similar process in operation. What Cézanne started Picasso continued to develop. Pictures **1, 2,** and **3** come from about the same period of his life. He was then still walking in Cézanne's footsteps. Pictures **4, 5,** and **6** mark the next, analytic, stage. Analysis is taken a stage further; forms are broken up and almost dissolved. (We must remember that scientists of the period were doing comparable things and thinking comparable thoughts.) Eventually, over the years, Picasso learned to put the analysed pieces together again, purified and in a different order (synthetic period). In the final arrangement of a picture he may include views which cannot normally be obtained at the same time and from the same point of view, **7** to **10**. For example, the portrait, **7**, includes a view of the crown of the hat from above, the brim is seen from below, the nose in profile, the mouth in profile and from the front, one eye is seen from the front, the other from the side, but both pupils from the front. In short, the painting reveals a changing angle of view. The analysis of form has brought us to the idea of movement, which we shall take up again later.

1 2

3 4

5 6

The developments we have been discussing on the last four pages span about seventy years. While they were taking place a similar kind of analysis and search for basic shapes was occurring in architecture, interior and industrial design. As in the case of picture **1**, page 92, one part of society was concerned with superficial values only, **1**, **2**, **7**. Form and space, which the Renaissance had worked so hard to establish, are here completely ignored, swamped by excessive ornaments. The room, **1**, can no longer be experienced as space, nor the objects, **2**, as forms; we are utterly confused by them. But there were some who felt oppressed by such environments and they endeavoured to find a saner approach. William Morris was one of the first to point the way. His designs for wallpaper, **8**, fabrics and furniture try to show us that behind all the welter of over-decoration simple, basic shapes and patterns do exist, and that these simple shapes are efficient. Cézanne had shown that basic shapes exist in nature. Voysey, an English architect, designed the interior, **3**, the cruet, **4**, the house, **5**, and the chair, **6**, all about the turn of the century. What a contrast to **1** and **2**! The hall, **3**, can be seen as space. The rails enclosing the staircase are a touch of genius, defining the volume of the staircase in the lightest, gentlest way without intruding too much into the space of the hall. The house, the cruet and the chair have definite, crisp forms. Ornaments and patterns are derived from the materials themselves or from the function of the objects. Notice especially the chimney tops and the dovetailing on the chairback. Looking at these objects one can feel a process of analysis similar to Cézanne's, a process which was common to many aspects of life and (enlightened) thought of this period. The early English pioneers like Voysey were important to what was later to grow into the Modern Movement. Architects such as Adolf Loos in Austria, **9**, and Erich Mendelsohn in Germany, **10**, carried this spirit into the twentieth century and gave it a more twentieth-century character.

8

9 **10**

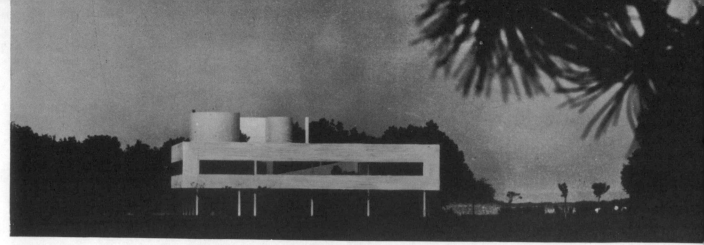

1

2

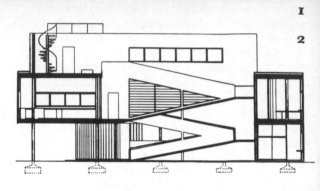

3

We have examined two streams of development, the analytical process in painting, and a similar process in architecture and interior and industrial design. Both tried to find certain basic truths. On the surface these two streams may seem to have little in common, but they often supported and confirmed each other, at times they met and joined forces. For instance, the aims of both can be seen again and again in the work of Le Corbusier. The building, **1**, was designed to be functionally efficient. The drawing, **2**, shows the arrangement of rooms and other spaces. The round wind breaks on the sun-roof, the rectangular bulk of the house, pierced by slot-like windows, the pillars (pilotis) which raise the living area above the hall and garage, all these seem to be necessary for the efficient working of the house. Let us remember that it was Le Corbusier who coined the phrase 'A house is a machine for living in'. But this is not the whole story of the design of the house. Picture **3** shows a painting of bottles and a glass made by Le Corbusier at about the same time, 1928. It can be seen to be derived from the painting of Cézanne and Picasso. Le Corbusier investigates here the geometrical relationships between round and rectangular shapes, and the transparency of glass allows us to see these relationships more easily. Other paintings from this period show a similar preoccupation. If we now look at the other photographs of various views of the interior of the house, **4**, **5**, **6**, we begin to realise how much his painting must have helped and influenced him in his architecture. The relationship between cylinder and slab, **1** and **6**, is similar to that in the painting. The relationship between the cylindrical shaft of the spiral staircase breaking through various horizontal planes, seen from the outside through a wall of glass, **4**, and the relationship of the shaft to another curved wall of glass, **5**, **6**, have also been derived from the thoughts which went into the painting. If you look closely you will find other points which correspond. Although this house was designed to fulfil certain functions, the way in which the shapes were arranged is in part due to the visual analysis which the architect learned from the painting of his time. If we look again at his much later Ronchamp chapel (pages 82 to 85, Part Two), we can see that apart from the functional requirements (discussed on those pages) certain visual requirements were also satisfied. This house is not an isolated example, it is typical of the way in which visual ideas influence the shapes of things we make.

Since the Renaissance artists have at various times studied the problem of showing movement without ever solving it. In picture **2** the artist tried to create an impression of a man walking by showing two stages of his progress. Watteau, the artist who painted picture **1**, describes movement of a more refined nature. The first couple on the right is sitting down. Next to them another couple is seen rising, the man helping the lady to her feet. The third couple is beginning to walk away, and so on, a whole succession of couples leads all the way down the bank to the water. Although the dress varies this is obviously meant to be the same couple throughout, and so logical is the sequence that it links up into one long movement as complicated as a quadrille.

2

But these paintings only *imply* movement, they do not *portray* it. That had to wait until the idea of movement became more important in people's minds, when the Industrial Revolution created not only the need but also the means for the movement of goods and for cheap travel. Movement had a special meaning in the new factories. Machine efficiency was foremost in the minds of industrialists. Workshops of earlier periods, **3,** were not really planned in our sense of the word. The layout simply came about, and time lost or gained by different arrangements was not taken into account. But if a factory owner was not to lose money, machines which were expensive to build and buy had to be used in such a way that they produced as much as possible. New methods, often the result of prolonged study, were devised for arranging machines, and these layouts, **4,** were the forerunners of the assembly lines of the present day. The aim was to eliminate as far as possible waste of movement and of time.

3

4

In addition to investigating the movement of the manufactured article, engineers studied the individual movements of the people who worked the machines, with the object of simplifying these movements and increasing output. Scientific methods of analysis were used in these investigations. To make the results easily understood, three dimensional models of the paths of movements of workers' hands, **5,** were sometimes made, and the idea that movement could be represented in graphic and even sculptural form was first evolved. This method of analysing movement – in a more refined form – is still used today in the design of machines, **6**.

5   **6**

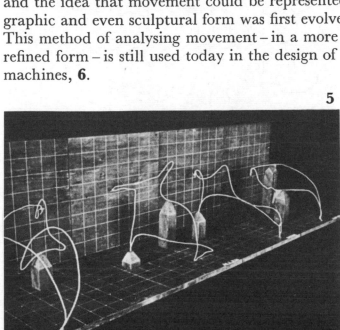

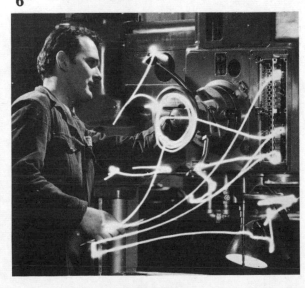

Doctors and scientists had already been investigating the movements of human beings and animals from a scientific or medical point of view. When the photographic camera and other pieces of apparatus were perfected these analyses of movement could be carried out with a great deal of precision. Soon there was a flood of diagrams and graphs describing movements of all kinds. The idea of movement was very much in the air.

1 *is a stereoscopic photograph of the path of a light fastened to the back of a man walking away from the camera. If you look at this picture from only a few inches away and focus your eyes into the distance until the two images coincide you will see the path in three dimensions.* **4** *is a photograph of the successive positions of a strip fastened to the leg of a man running. It shows the rhythm of the movement.* **2** *shows the path described by a light fastened to the wing of a pigeon, and* **3** *the successive positions of the pigeon's body and wings, seen from above. These complicated movements can also be combined. The three-dimensional model,* **5**, *was made from data compiled from investigations such as those made in* **2** *and* **3**.

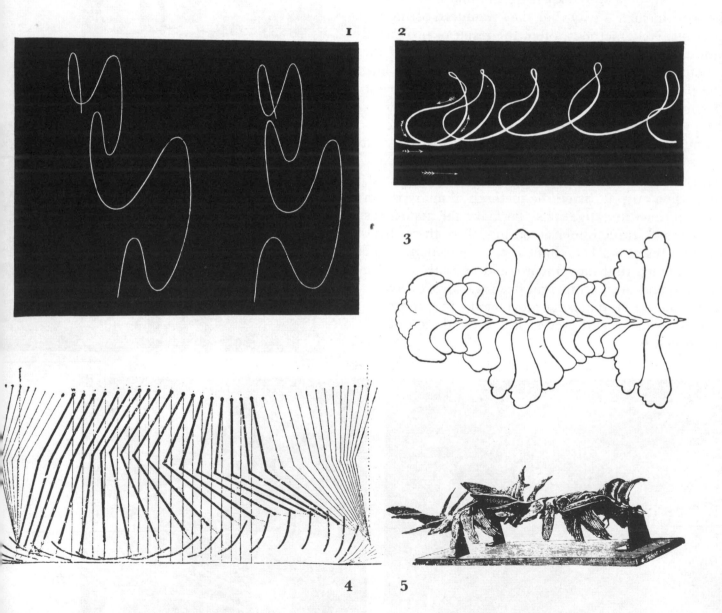

1

2

3

4   5

This was the atmosphere in which artists too worked
out their analyses of movement. The painting, **6**, by
Duchamp, shows a figure descending a staircase. It
is not so much a painting of a figure as of its
movement: its character and rhythm. The sculpture
of a walking man, **7**, by Boccioni, was made more
than half a century ago and tackles a similar problem.
We could compare these two works with pictures **4**
and **5** on page 104, which we might describe as their
scientific counterparts. Considering the mood of the
times, it was not unnatural or unreasonable that
artists should want to explain movement, but it is
clear that they were interested not only in the physical
effect of movement but also in its effect on our
emotions.

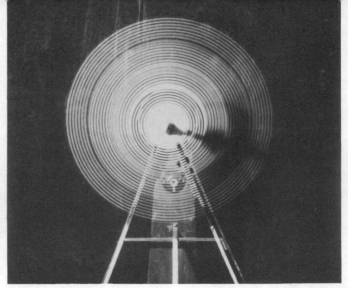

2

1

3

A-20 BENDS ITS NOSE UP IN CLIMB

FAST POWER-STOP CONTRACTS A-20

B-24 BENDS HEAVILY IN PULL-OUT

VIOLENT MANEUVER DISTORTS B-25

B-25 STARTS BEND FOR A PULL-OUT

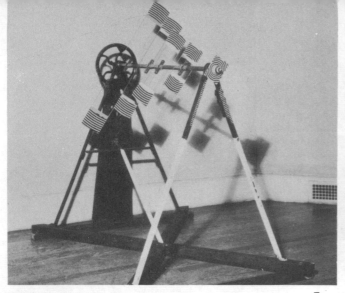

4

The machine, **1**, is one which the painter Duchamp used in his investigations of the visual effect of movement, here rotary movement. **2** shows one of the patterns obtained with it. Investigations of this kind led to various methods of portraying movement. The visual discoveries of certain artists have influenced the visual language of our time in many ways, most of which we do not realise. The blurring of the photograph of the moving car, **5**, might be considered a flaw, but through the work of artists like Duchamp and Boccioni we have learned to understand and accept such pictures as the representation of movement. They have helped to give us our visual language. A person living in the Renaissance or the Middle Ages would not have understood this picture because it would not have formed part of his visual language. The drawing, **4**, from an advertisement, also shows the effect of the work of these early pioneers. This is certainly not a great work of art, but it indicates the movement which is such an essential part of the chair, as well as its form. **3** is an instruction chart for pilots. Through distortion of form it explains the effect of certain controls on the movement of the plane. Do you think words could achieve the same effect?

5

In addition to the analysis of form and the analysis of movement, the nineteenth century also saw the beginnings of the analysis of the human mind. Psycho-analysis, the science developed by Sigmund Freud, analyses man's behaviour and state of mind. Freud discovered that behind our conscious self there is another power, which he called the subconscious mind, and that this part of our being is responsible for many of our actions. Echoes of a long-forgotten past are contained in the subconscious – our own past and the past of the whole human race. What happens to us throughout our lives – and especially during childhood – leaves its mark on the subconscious, even if we do not remember the exact happenings or consider them unimportant. On another level the fears and magic of man's earliest history can still be found in each one of us.

Millions of people still read their horoscopes and, however secretly, believe much of what they read. If you took a photograph of someone you know and, using a pin, pierced it through the person's eyes, would that leave you quite unmoved or would you perhaps feel some pangs? There can be no doubt that such ancient superstitions and desires influence our actions. We read on page 76 that we see only what we want or expect to see. We cannot possibly see in the sense that a camera sees, for our minds will 'process' what we see and even distort it to make it conform with our knowledge and experience. But we know from the findings of psycho-analysis that our subconscious minds reach back to the beginnings of the human race and that we are affected by events much more deeply than had ever been suspected. People began to realise that the effect of our minds on our vision is an extremely subtle and complicated affair.

A group of artists tried to get a fuller understanding of man by making use of the teachings of Freud. They did this in several ways and one of them was the use of images which can be described as dreamlike.

The subconscious is normally well below the surface of our minds and we are never aware of it, although it controls our actions. But in our dreams it becomes 'visible', while our 'normal' self ceases to exercise any

6. *This house, built in America at the time of the Gold Rush (the end of the last century) has a watchful eye painted on its roof-light. Did the people who lived there really believe in its power? Like the readers of horoscopes, they probably hoped – and in their innermost hearts believed – that it had a magic power. However 'modern' we may think ourselves, we are never far from such beliefs.*

6

1

2

control over us, and dream events and relationships fall into different patterns from those which we expect in the real world.

By using such images these artists hoped to attain not mere realism, as the artists of the past, but super-realism, or *surrealism*. The surrealists, as these artists were called, were not interested in the superficial appearance of things, or in people's superficial behaviour. They tried to find out what really moved us to behave in the way we do. They sought to explore the life of the mind and of the emotions.

Their hopes were not entirely fulfilled but their work opened up many wonderful possibilities. They influenced many other artists and enriched the vocabulary of our visual language beyond measure.

Like other modern visual ideas Surrealism is not entirely new. The Surrealist landscape, by Max Ernst, 2, entitled 'The Eye of Silence', is a strange dream-like setting of a human figure amidst unreal-looking shapes somehow resembling rocks. If we look at a detail of a painting by Leonardo da Vinci, 1, we can experience a similar feeling, or at least an attempt on the artist's part to achieve a similar effect. But whereas in the painting by Leonardo we can still recognise everything we see, Ernst has dispensed with any imitation of reality. Instead, his shapes seem to remind us of things which we cannot quite recall. We are therefore forced to draw on the depths of our minds to 'read' this picture. 'The Whole Town', 3, another picture by Max Ernst, also suggests a landscape we might have seen somewhere and the feelings it aroused. In this way Surrealist paintings probe and stimulate our innermost emotions and thoughts.

3

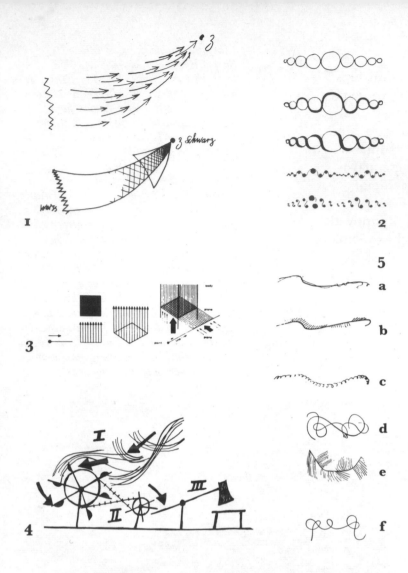

If any artist can be described as truly representative of the first half of the twentieth century, it must surely be Paul Klee. In his work the visual and philosophical ideas of our time are combined, developed and exploited. His influence on the visual language of our generation is probably stronger than that of any other artist. The posters you see in the streets, the road signs and shop signs, diagrams and cartoons in books and magazines, the patterns of fabric designs and those executed in other materials, many of these owe a great debt to Klee's work. The lessons and observations which he wrote down during the time he was active as a teacher show that he developed his visual ideas through the modern analytic method. The arrows, **1**, converging on a point, express movement; they can also be summed up in a master arrow in which the gradation from white to black appears to add speed. The analysis of a sequence of shapes reveals surprising rhythms, **2**. A point in motion produces a line, a line in motion a plane, a plane in motion a solid shape, **3**. This is here shown as a simple visual progression. He also investigated the relationships between lines: between, for instance, a principal line and a subsidiary one, **5a**, **5d**, or many subsidiary ones, **5b**, **5e**. Single lines can describe a rhythm within a larger rhythm, **5c**, or just make detours, **5f**. Such knowledge could be put to use in diagrams of a purely mechanical nature, **4**, (wind drives windmill – wheel – hammer) so that no words are required. Klee was particularly interested in re-creating more subtle and human ideas, such as those of the next three drawings, **6**, **7**, **9**. The

6   7

8

9

drawing of a burglar at work, **6**, describes not only his action but also the stealth with which it is carried out. The cartoon-like drawing of a man, **7**, expresses the man's overbearing, pompous character better than words ever could. Compare the use of the exclamation mark with **5**, page 62. **9** describes the character of an old musician – the violin, his life's companion, has become part of him. The painting, **8**, 'The Ships set Sail', has a magic derived from Klee's years of research and analysis. The pictorial use of the arrow, a device we could hardly manage without (see page 62), is Klee's own invention and should serve as a reminder of our great indebtedness to him.

2 3

4

1

In 1937, during the Spanish Civil War, the Basque town of Guernica was destroyed by planes of the Fascist forces. Many civilians – men, women, and children – were killed. Picasso painted a picture as a protest against this outrage; in it he gave vent to his feelings of horror at the raid, **5**. Ideas of horror and of suffering were not new to him (see page 126, Part One), but he made numerous further sketches as preliminary drawings for this work, not to be copied into the picture but so as to familiarise himself even further with the subject matter, and the visual expression of the feelings he wished to portray, **2**. In the same way his great compatriot, Goya, drew on his own experience of war and death **4**, when he painted a similar subject, **6**. When the invading French armies shot a great number of Spanish citizens in Madrid on the 3rd of May, 1808, Goya witnessed the event and felt as outraged as Picasso did at the destruction of Guernica. In his painting a well-disciplined line of faceless soldiers point their steely-cold, efficient rifles and bayonets at an irregular, miserable mass of humanity in various states of emotion: heroism, fear, despair, incredulity The contrast between the precision of the military group and the shapelessness of the group of condemned men makes the artist's message very powerful. The events and feelings are described in the visual language of Goya's time.

Picasso felt similar emotions but he used a different visual language. Because the visual language of the twentieth century allowed him to dispense with realism (perspective, light and shade, modelling, etc.) Picasso's message emerges in a more concentrated and powerful form than Goya's. Every line, every square inch of his painting has an important contribution to make. Look at the hand in the bottom left-hand corner: its shape and pattern of lines suggest suffering of the most savage kind. The woman immediately above holding a dead child is stricken with intense grief, the figure on the extreme right is filled with fear and despair.

Picasso is a Spaniard and the imagery of bullfighting comes readily to his mind. Goya, too, had experience the savagery of the bullfight, **1**. Picasso used this idea symbolically in his picture of Guernica. The presence of the gored, screaming horse and of the bull increases the feeling of bestiality. In every part of the painting Picasso describes modern experience in modern visual language. For instance, the head of the figure rushing in through the door shows distress, and at the same time the inrushing movement is accentuated by a distortion of the head. **3**, a speed photograph of a tennis player, shows a distortion similar to that arrived at by Picasso in his painting of the head. By making use of every device that the modern visual language had put at his disposal, Picasso recorded not merely the destruction of Guernica, but also the suffering that went with it, the effect of the event on the human mind and emotions.

5

1

No consideration of our visual language would be complete if it did not include the language of the moving picture: the film. This is an entirely new visual medium and it probably comes nearer than any other to reflecting the true spirit of our age. Its unique contribution to our visual language is that it can describe human beings and movement in a way that has never before been possible. The film director has many devices at his command. He can use close-ups of faces or details of objects and actions, unusual angles of vision and carefully planned sequences. He can even use drawings and diagrams. By all these means and many others he can lay the whole world before us and help us to understand the workings of the human mind.

3

2

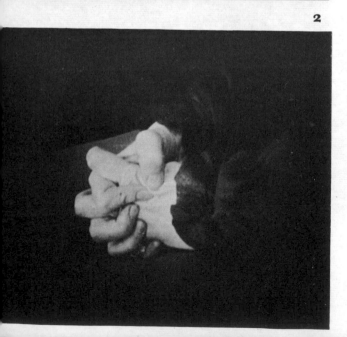

*The earliest film makers already understood the basic language of the film: a visual language. Consider, for instance, the two stills, from 'Intolerance', **1, 2**, made by Griffith in 1917. The scene is a courtroom in which sentence is passed on a man. His wife hears the sentence with little sign of emotion, **1**, but the close-up, **2**, shows us how the nails of her clasped hands dig into her flesh. We realise her suppressed torment, of which perhaps no one in the courtroom was aware. By using the devices peculiar to the cinema, the film director has given us an insight into a situation, which in real life we might not have noticed. He has shown us what goes on below the surface. Imagine how a novelist or a playwright might have expressed this by using the devices of the novel or of the drama. The quality of the photography has certainly been improved and technical refinements have been introduced since the early days of the film but its visual language was established almost from the outset.*

Here are some of the many devices which a film director may use. An unusual angle of vision may increase the tension of a scene, **3**. (Compare this to the similar effect which Mantegna achieves in 'The Agony in the Garden', **1**, page 89.) A close-up, **4**, may take us closer to a person's character or the effect of the action. We may see the sweat on someone's forehead, for instance. The cinema can also give gripping reality to scenes from the past. Notice the extreme detail of picture **5**, which shows one of the less pleasing aspects of eighteenth-century London. Picture **6** shows an example of the way in which films can create atmosphere. The wet cobbles, the mysterious side-lighting, whose source is hidden and which makes the cobbles look even wetter, the shabby walls and shutters, the loneliness of the figure against the grandiose architecture of the past, all these help to create an atmosphere which is peculiar to the place and time which this film, 'The Third Man', describes: Vienna during the first cruel winter after the war. In picture **7**, a still from 'Last Year in Marienbad', the spacious geometry of a French garden serves as a setting for the main actors. They are standing still and their long shadows fall on the white gravel. Yet the shrubs cast no shadows. We cannot cope with this strange spectacle by using the ordinary laws of logic. The scene stimulates us somewhat as the Surrealist painting does (**2**, page 108). While **6** appeals to us through the senses by recreating surfaces, textures, atmosphere, **7** addresses itself to the subconscious mind. Two different approaches, both equally suited to the language of the cinema.

4 **5**

6 **7**

4

8

9

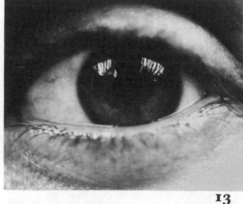

12

13

16

17

We must not forget that the film consists of moving pictures and not of stills. The landscape, **1**, may be further investigated by allowing the camera to move into it, **2**, **3**, **4**; the park scene similarly, **5** to **9**. By moving the camera in, the director lets us see more and more detail, each stage revealing something new. In the final close-up, **9**, we are looking at a part of the scene reflected in the eye. The sequence is made up of pictures taken from different distances (long shots, close-ups) to show both setting and details. You can also tell from the different angle of each picture that the camera did not move towards the man in a straight line but in a wide arc. The pictures of the sequence therefore let us see different aspects of the same thing. It is in fact rather similar to the visual analysis in Picasso's paintings, **7**, page 97, for instance. By using such methods a film can re-create complex patterns, such as those of streets and even whole towns. Pictures **10** to **17** show the different views which can be combined to form a more complicated whole, in this case a certain quarter of London; **10**, a street market; **11**, the character of a stall holder; **12**, **13**, some of the customers; **14**, the backs and **15**, the fronts of houses further down the street; **16**, a close-up of **15**; **17**, another street round the corner. From such a film we may form an idea of the many-sided character of a place and of the people who live in it. The impressions we get from a film do not depend primarily on the sharpness of the lens of the camera, but on the sharpness of the director's perception and the skill with which each shot is composed and whole sequences built up to express this perception.

These two pages show a few shots from a
sequence in the film 'Tom Jones', directed by
Tony Richardson. The subject of this sequence is
a hunt in eighteenth-century England. **1**, the
servants prepare the refreshments; **2**, the hunters
arrive; **3**, their horses; **4**, refreshments are
poured; **5**, **6**, **7**, **8**, **9**, various aspects of the
crowd of drinkers; **10**, the hounds are let out;
11, **12**, the hunters follow; **13**, one of the
hunters; **14**, the landscape in which the scene
takes place; **15**, the hunt grows fast and furious;
16, **17**, a horseman breaks through the thicket
and, **18**, disappears; **19**, **20**, the hounds after the
prey; **21**, Tom Jones chases after a runaway
horse and **22** rescues a lady; **23**, they fall to the
ground. This sequence falls into two obvious
halves; the leisurely pace of the hunt assembling
contrasted with the speed and excitement which

follows. In the first part, **1** to **9**, detailed observations show the different characters and the activities of the crowd. In the second part (**10** to **23**), speed and movement are the main ingredients. Examination of detail is impossible, shapes are distorted by speed, **15**, **20**, and even dissolve, **18**. Like a full stop, the fall, **23**, brings this exciting sequence to a close. It is easy to see, even from these stills, that the director has used the devices and the vocabulary of the film, its visual language, to great effect. By building up the work of his cameramen in a definite order, by judiciously placing different shots according to his master plan, he has told a story in the particular language of the film; it could not have been told like this in any other medium.

The best craftsmen through their sensitivity and imagination have always found the most suitable shapes for their purpose. A good film director will find the best form of a film in much the same way as a potter finds the best form of a vessel. It would be possible to make a film in the manner of a play, as though the action were taking place on a stage, but this would be unlikely to be the most efficient way of telling the story on film; just as a plastic cup in the form of a pottery cup would be inefficient. It would not make use of the special resources of the moving picture while suffering all its drawbacks. When we see a film we must learn to judge it not only by its story but also by the extent to which the director has succeeded in using the devices of the film, some of which we have mentioned, in order to express the story in the most effective way. Any progress in film making must be considered in these terms and not in terms of panoramic screens or stereophonic sound which only attempt to make films more realistic. Realism as such is not necessarily a good thing. Nothing can compete with the realism of life itself and any attempt to do so can only fail. The purpose of the film should be to describe and comment in order to help us to understand more about life.

The opening sequence from the film 'Great Expectations' also shows how a film director (David Lean) tells a story in visual terms. A boy runs along the shore towards us past two gibbets. He looks over a wall, then climbs over it into a cemetery. He walks to one of the graves and lays some flowers on it. The wind howls in the trees. The boy is disturbed by the uncanny atmosphere. A noise makes him look up. He sees the menacing form of a willow creaking in the wind. The boy is frightened and turns to run away when a hand, apparently from nowhere, grips his throat. He screams. He stares into the coarse, sweaty, unshaven face of a convict who shakes him by the neck. The gibbets of the opening shot symbolise the idea of crime – an important theme throughout the film – the convict introduces it in a more definite form. Through the clever construction of the sequence we, like the boy, experience a real shock at the sudden unexpected appearance of the convict. Crime is introduced into the film with the violence which such a subject demands.

The cartoon film stands half way between cinema and painting. It uses devices which are closely related to both. In this example the relationship to painting is especially strongly marked. A scientist is speaking to a colleague but what he says 'goes in through one ear and out through the other'.

To sum up

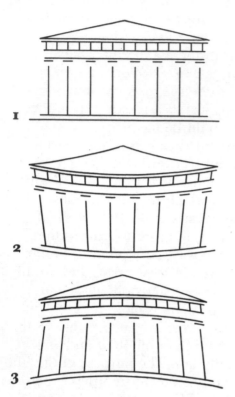

The appearance of a Greek temple expresses the Greek ideal of reason and the Greek sense of refined balance. It incorporates several perfectly balanced relationships: between the horizontals and verticals, between solids and spaces (that is between the solid forms, e.g. columns, and the space between them), between light and shade. It is perhaps the most perfect type of building ever invented. Diagram 1 shows the main lines of the Parthenon at Athens, 4. Had it been built exactly as in this diagram it would have appeared as shown (in an exaggerated way) in diagram 2. This is wholly due to optical illusions. In order to counteract this tendency the architect distorted the structure. Diagram 3 shows the way in which it was actually built. The horizontals are about 2½ inches higher in the centre than at the sides. The uprights lean towards the centre, the outer columns by about 2·65 inches. Remember that although it was built in this distorted way we see it as in 1. This shows not only the exquisite visual sense of the Greeks but also their horror at anything unbalanced. It is easy to believe that they considered ugliness to be one of the worst crimes.

As we have seen, a visual language is an unconscious attempt to weave many strands into one fabric: the strands of experience, of science, of philosophy, of religion, of economics, of emotion, of instinct. It is a natural growth, in which thought and feeling work together to create a harmonious pattern. When each individual person understands the visual language of his age, it becomes an important influence not only on individuals but on the entire society in which they live. It expresses the whole of man. As man's outlook on life and his society change, he must seek new ways of expressing himself. Visual language can never remain the same; it must change with man's ideas and condition.

For instance, the Greek view of life was essentially reasonable and reasoned. The Greeks discussed things amongst themselves. They built their temples and carved their statues according to mathematical laws. They governed themselves by a system of government to which they gave the name of democracy, a fusion of thought and sense. Even their religion was reasonable. Their visual language expressed their balanced view of life. The arch and the dome were known to other peoples at the time when Greek civilisation was at its height, but the Greeks made no use of them in their building. These forms were out of harmony with the level-headed attitude of the Greeks. Huge domes would have offended their feeling for balance. If they could have known the building methods of the medieval architects they would have been equally unimpressed. A Greek approached his religion with his mind and not with his emotion, and religious services in the Christian sense were unknown to him. The structure of a Gothic cathedral would have been as useless to a Greek as its visual impact would have been disagreeable.

A true visual language expresses both thought and feeling. At the same time it creates a truly human, harmonious pattern, for it combines conscious and unconscious activities. Such a visual language embodies the scientific and technological skills of an age and at the same time expresses man's feelings. The visual languages of primitive man, of the highly civilised

Greeks, of the citizens of medieval towns, or of men of the Renaissance are all based on this blend of thought and feeling. Each one evolved as a means of expression for its own time, its own way of thinking and feeling, and it would have been meaningless in any other age. On pages 77–78 we likened the evolution of a visual language to the painting of a picture. Now imagine that as you are finishing your painting someone looks over your shoulder and is struck by the colours in it. He would like to paint a picture like that, so he sits down and copies your colours. What do you think will be the result? Perhaps some people will be taken in and will put his picture on the same level as yours, but others will see and feel that it is second-hand and insincere. Your painting is an unconscious and therefore honest expression of yourself, while his is a sham.

We can apply this simile to a whole period. The nineteenth century, for example, looked over the shoulders of past centuries and tried to recapture their glories. The dishonesty of such acts makes itself felt sooner or later. Because the nineteenth century did not relate thought to feeling, the conscious to the unconscious mind, it had no visual language in the true sense, but only a visual gibberish. It tried to revive the visual languages of the Egyptian, Greek and Roman civilisations, as well as of all the centuries from the eleventh to the eighteenth. A writer of the nineteenth century, perhaps more clear-sighted than his contemporaries, wrote: 'One thing is pretty certain, nobody will want to revive the nineteenth century.' If a Greek of, say, fifth century Athens, would have been displeased by the sight of a Gothic building, how much more would he have disliked the sight of buildings in mixed styles. Unfortunately this is a sight which most of us have to endure daily, surrounded as we are by what the nineteenth century has left behind. This mixture of visual languages had the opposite effect to the visual languages of other ages. Instead of unifying thoughts and feelings, it drove a wedge between the thoughts and feelings of people of the nineteenth century. Today we are still suffering the after effects of the visual and mental muddle of that period.

The legacy of the nineteenth century

Only by being honest with ourselves can we develop a true twentieth century visual language, which will make our lives complete and harmonious. Although a new visual language is now within our reach, there are still many obstacles in the way. After a long period of making do without a true visual language, we have forgotten how to use one. We are no longer aware of the simple visual laws which governed man's creations in the past, nor do we fully realise the special needs of today's conditions. Because most people do not understand the vocabulary and the grammar of the visual language of our times it is often misused. The greater part of the new environment we are building is still incoherent and muddled.

There are other obstacles. For instance, many people think of their motor cars as a sign of superiority over their fellow human beings. Cars designed and produced to satisfy this wish are unlikely to be efficient vehicles and cannot be an honest expression of their function. More often than not, houses, furniture and most other commodities are produced in a similar spirit. This suits those manufacturers who are only interested in selling as many of their products as possible by whatever means. Their advertising, therefore, often appeals to our less admirable ambitions. How can a true visual language develop in these conditions?

1

2

The Triumph 2000: sleek controls, elegant body. As much at home in the paddock at Silverstone as outside church this morning

The architect who designed **1** misunderstood the principles of modern architecture. The dreariness of the pattern and the shape, which express neither function nor structure, is overpowering. The reinforced concrete bridge, **2**, has the pattern and shape of a stone bridge – notice especially the shape of the piers, which is typical of stonework. The radio set, **3**, might seem very modern at first glance, but a closer examination will show that it is merely intended to appeal to people who want to be thought modern. Is there any functional reason for its ungainly shape? The television set in a 'Queen Anne' cabinet, **4**, might be compared to a nuclear reactor in a half-timbered Tudor building. The people who made it seem to have been ashamed of our age. It is true that the controls of the motor car, **5**, are very well designed, but does the newspaper comment below the picture make sense? Do you think the writer's reasons for liking the car are the right ones? The clock on the automatic tea maker, **6**, looks as awkward as the handles must feel. The hands of a clock move in a circular motion, therefore the face should be round. The various clocks shown in picture **7** betray ideas like those which prompted the comment in **5**. Can you find any fault with the figures? The overall shapes of the clocks are arbitrary and not in any way related to their function or mechanism. Compare these pictures to those on pages 78, 79 and 86, 87. Do you think this group shows anything approaching a modern visual language?

I

The true visual language of our age may be seen in these pictures.
We have discovered how our interest in the inner workings of nature
has led to the idea of analysis and how visual analysis of form led to
simpler shapes, unadorned by inessential or unrelated ornaments.
The working parts of an object and the patterns which they form
now provide the interest for which in former times artificial
embellishments were applied. The Victorians built factories with
turrets, battlements, pointed arches and pediments. The modern
factory, **1**, derives its pleasing shapes from an analysis of the
manufacturing process. All its forms, internal as well as external,
are the result of this analysis. This is not the whole story: the
architect was also interested in the relationships of planes, shapes
and patterns. The exceptionally clear form of this building is due to
visual analysis. Compare it with the house by Corbusier, pages
100–101. The new way of thinking is being applied in many ways
and its effects can be seen in many man-made objects, from
buildings to such things as the telephone which we discussed
on page 35.

*Analysis of form and structure, **2**, has led to an economy of means
and in many cases to a breaking up of form: the aluminium struts
indicate and outline a form which is mostly air. The sculpture
'The Unknown Political Prisoner', **3**, shows how an artist used a
similar analysis of form to express feeling.*

*The pictures on these pages show some objects which employ the
technology of our day to express the ideas of our day; a union of
methods and imagination; of thought and feeling. We have seen
that only on such principles can a new visual language evolve, as
was the case with the visual languages of Gothic and Renaissance
times.*

The construction, design and appearance of our towns,
buildings, machines, books and films will combine in
a harmonious pattern only if we learn to understand
the spirit of our time and find the visual language to
express it. But before this can happen we must complete
the task of abandoning values from the past which are
no longer relevant to our age.

*The sculpture by Henry Moore symbolises the new
visual language. A human figure with an ancient and
eternal look, apparently as old as human history and yet of
today, silhouetted against a new block of flats. The spirit of
man and his physical environment are given visual expression.*

In the paintings of Giotto we can see the unmistakable beginnings of the visual language of the Renaissance and a breaking away from the medieval visual language. The many different poses of the various persons taking part in the drama of the Deposition (above), the emotions expressed, the modelling and foreshortening of faces and bodies, all these indicate different values and a different mental climate from that of medieval times (top, opposite). The central figure with outstretched arms would have been barely intelligible to the medieval eye. His right arm, groping into the depth of the painting, seems to initiate the Renaissance conquest of space.